£ 12

GW00836200

HANDLIST OF ANGLO-SAXON MANUSCRIPTS

A List of Manuscripts and Manuscript Fragments

Written or Owned in England up to 1100

MEDIEVAL AND RENAISSANCE TEXTS AND STUDIES

VOLUME 241

HANDLIST OF ANGLO-SAXON MANUSCRIPTS

A List of Manuscripts and Manuscript Fragments

Written or Owned in England up to 1100

BY

HELMUT GNEUSS

Arizona Center for Medieval and Renaissance Studies
Tempe, Arizona
2001

© Copyright 2001
Helmut Gneuss

This book is made to last.
It is smythe-sewn
and printed on acid-free paper
to library specifications

Printed in the United States of America

CONTENTS

HANDLIST OF ANGLO-SAXON MANUSCRIPTS

A List of Manuscripts and Manuscript Fragments

Written or Owned in England up to 1100

Introduction

The project: its origin and aims

Scholars and students with an interest in Anglo-Saxon England and its culture have been fortunate in having been provided with catalogues of manuscripts containing Old English texts in prose or verse, glosses and glossaries for over three centuries now: a pioneering list by the great antiquary and philologist George Hickes was followed by the admirable *Catalogus* of Humfrey Wanley, a palaeographer whose achievement appears to have been largely ignored on the European Continent. His work was only superseded when Neil Ker's masterly *Catalogue of Manuscripts Containing Anglo-Saxon* appeared two and a half centuries later, describing more than four hundred manuscripts, 189 of these in great detail.[1]

But the usefulness of a complete inventory of *all* surviving manuscripts and fragments of the period, including those exclusively in Latin, must have been obvious to many, as can be seen from a remark by Wanley:

> Cum primum ad hoc opus me accincturus essem, suadentibus Amicis, Literaturae *Saxonicae* qui cultores sunt, *Latinos* Libros, Chartasque omnes qui ab Anglo-Saxonibus scripti, vel descripti erant, in Catalogo ponere decrevi; sed Consilium mutavi, ubi primum majorem illorum esse numerum sensi, quam qui in Catalogo, quem mente designaram, contineri potuit.
>
> Wanley, *Catalogus*, Sig. c2.

The need for a full inventory became clear to me in the course of my work on psalter glosses and the office hymns, when I realised that such work ought to take into account all extant liturgical books from Anglo-Saxon England; this resulted in a classified list published much later.[2] In the meantime, however, a book by Professor Ogilvy had appeared that seemed to supply what was needed, yet it turned out to be unreliable in too many ways, as was duly pointed out in the reviews.[3]

Partly as a consequence, I began to compile what was later published, at the instigation of my dear friend Peter Clemoes, as „A Preliminary list of manuscripts written or owned in England up to 1100."[4] It was 'preliminary' indeed, not only because the individual entries (covering 947 items) had to be so brief as to fit into an article in a periodical, but also because there were inevitable shortcomings, reflecting the state of scholarship at the time, particularly

1

with regard to dating and localizing books, shortcomings of which I was well aware. But the substance, in the main, seemed sound, because I was able to rely not only on what I had seen myself, but especially on the recently published work by Neil Ker, T. A. M. Bishop, the volumes of the „Survey of Manuscripts Illuminated in the British Isles" by Jonathan Alexander and Elzbieta Temple, and, of course, *Codices Latini Antiquiores*, to mention only the most important contributions in the field.[5] For manuscripts imported from the Continent, my then colleague in Munich, Bernhard Bischoff, generously as always shared with me his unrivalled knowledge of continental book-production, in my case especially that of ninth-century France.

Work on preparing the „Preliminary list" had to be based on what was known in the sixties and seventies. In the meantime, the situation has changed. There has been an ever-increasing literature on Anglo-Saxon manuscripts: books, articles, new catalogues of manuscript collections (Lincoln, Hereford, and above all Neil Ker's *Medieval Manuscripts in British Libraries*), catalogues of dated and datable manuscripts, exhibition catalogues, facsimile and printed editions, and, most recently, the series of *Anglo-Saxon Manuscripts in Microfiche Facsimile*,[6] while considerable progress has been made in the study of palaeography and codicology; the Department of Anglo-Saxon, Norse and Celtic in the University of Cambridge has been one of the leading centres of research in these fields.[7] All this has been utilized for the present *Handlist*, which is a completely revised, updated and expanded version of the „Preliminary list", including numerous new items.

The last thirty or forty years have been marked by decisive progress of scholarship, but there have been other changes, too. Not a few manuscripts have changed owners and can now be found not only in Europe and the United States, but also in Japan and New Zealand. Numerous new items have become known, mainly fragments and *membra disiecta* of manuscripts, which sometimes turned up in unlikely places, like the leaf from an eleventh-century psalter with interlinear Old English glosses recently found in a museum in Thuringia.[8] Spectacular finds like that of a complete Pontifical and Benedictional, discovered in 1970 in stables in Scotland, will no doubt remain the exception.[9]

There seems hardly any need to point out the problems involved in compiling a *Handlist of Anglo-Saxon Manuscripts* and in assessing the evidence for origin and provenance of books and fragments. Many of the manuscripts have never been properly catalogued and described or are treated in widely scattered publications. Much work remains to be done. Teresa Webber's masterly study of book-production in late eleventh and early twelfth-century Salisbury is a model of what we need. Birgit Ebersperger has shown how a group of manuscripts of widely differing origin but now kept together, in Paris, can be treated.[10] I can think of a considerable number of Anglo-Saxon manuscripts that would deserve detailed description and comprehensive treatment in monographs.

The reasons for our present-day difficulties with regard to the origin and provenance of Anglo-Saxon books are well-known: the lack of early library catalogues, as opposed to booklists;[11] the lack of early *ex libris* inscriptions; the grievous losses, particularly those caused by the suppression of the monasteries and the dispersal of their libraries. Very few books remain from what must have been well-stocked repositories of learning aAnd literature, like the Benedictine houses in Winchester, in Abingdon, Ely, Glastonbury, Malmesbury, Peterborough and Ramsey, the nunneries at Barking, Shaftesbury and Wilton, the cathedrals of London and York.[12]

A *Handlist* of manuscripts is not just an inventory; it should also serve as a contribution to our knowledge of book-production in Anglo-Saxon England, and to our understanding of the intellectual life of the period. I must here stress the word 'contribution', for we owe what can be listed today to the chance survival of about twelve hundred books and fragments of books when thousands of them must once have existed. Consequently, in order to form a realistic idea and picture of life and letters in Anglo-Saxon England, we shall have to combine the evidence of the surviving manuscripts with what source studies of various kinds can tell us, the study that is of translations, references, quotations, allusions and much else. Fortunately, two international projects devoted to such studies have made important progress in the past few years, have already yielded significant results, and are now nearing completion: „Fontes Anglo-Saxonici", with centres of research in Britain, and „Sources of Anglo-Saxon Literary Culture" („SASLC"), developed from Ogilvy's *Books known to the English*, but with a much wider scope.[13]

This is not the place to go into the various conclusions and results that a list of Anglo-Saxon manuscripts is likely to provide or at least to support. Let me just mention two points. One is ninth-century English book-production before the literary activities of King Alfred. Even if we take into account the vicissitudes in the life and preservation of early medieval manuscripts, we cannot ignore the fact that the number of surviving manuscripts written in England in the course of the ninth century,[14] compared to what survives from the eighth, and from the tenth century onwards, seems negligible, and this is not due to chance. The Viking invasions have often been considered the reason, but I believe I have been able to show elsewhere[15] that other, earlier developments played an important role, developments to which King Alfred expressly refers in his famous „Preface" to the translation of Pope Gregory's *Regula pastoralis*:

> Ða ic ða ðis eall gemunde, ða gemunde ic eac hu ic geseah, *ær ðæm ðe hit eall forhergod wære ond forbærned*, hu ða ciricean giond eall Angelcynn stodon maðma ond boca gefyldæ, ond eac micel mengeo Godes ðiowa; ond ða swiðe lytle fiorme ðara boca wiston, for ðæm ðe hie hiora nanwuht ongiotan ne meahton, for ðæm ðe hie næron on hiora agen geðiode awritene.[16]

We do, however, have a considerable number of ninth-century manuscripts with Anglo-Saxon provenance, but they are Continental, mainly French, and mainly imports of the English Benedictine Reform of the tenth century, a reform that was badly in need of outside assistance. Moreover, we should look at ninth-century Continental book-production, documented in Bernhard Bischoff's great catalogue (and catalogue materials) which Birgit Ebersperger is preparing for publication. Why do we have about 7000 extant books written (or added to) on the Continent in the ninth century, as against less than two dozen produced in England?[17]

My second example comes from the evidence of tenth and eleventh-century books. Devoted Anglo-Saxonists may have been saddened by what experts in the field like Neil Ker and T. A. M. Bishop had to say about the limitations of book-production and library holdings in late Anglo-Saxon England, i.e., from the time of King Alfred.[18] They noted especially the lack of adequate collections of patristic writings, mainly those by Ambrose, Augustine and Jerome. Gregory's works are an exception; but they are less voluminous and, above all, Gregory was considered „*pater Anglorum, doctor et apostolus.*"[19] It was a situation that had to be remedied sooner or later, and what I should call the Norman library programmes at the great centres like Canterbury, Durham, Exeter, Rochester and Salisbury go to show how the conspicuous gap was being filled in a very short time by organizing scriptoria or importing manuscripts from Normandy or elsewhere.

However, being an Anglo-Saxonist at heart myself, I feel that we should not ignore the Old English Benedictine achievement: nowhere else in Western Europe in the tenth and eleventh centuries would one have found – quite apart from England's early poetry and the vernacular

4

law codes – a collection of competent translations and adaptations of standard Latin texts, or the provision of continuous glosses, in all the country's leading libraries: the psalms and gospels, the hymns, the Rules of S. Benedict and of Chrodegang, the homiliary (largely that of Paul the Deacon), a martyrology, penitentials and medical texts, works by Gregory the Great (*Regula pastoralis*; *Dialogi*), by Augustine (*Soliloquia*), by Boethius (*Consolatio*), the historical works by Orosius and Bede, continued in the Anglo-Saxon Chronicle. And where else do we find a comprehensive, contrastive grammar of Latin like Ælfric's 'bestseller', again documented as such in the *Handlist*?[20] And, finally, only the Anglo-Saxonists among lexicographers of early Germanic dialects can build about 30000 entries on three million lexical tokens.

These few remarks will have to suffice in order to introduce what I hope will become a useful research tool, no matter how much more work in the field remains to be done.

Scope of the *Handlist*

The following have been included in the *Handlist*:

1. Manuscripts certainly written in England up to 1100. For the problem of late eleventh-century manuscripts, see below.

2. Manuscripts written in Scotland, Wales and Cornwall if they certainly or very probably reached England by 1100. A few manuscripts from those parts of Britain, written before 1100, have been included although it is unlikely that they had an English provenance, temporary or permanent, before the end of the eleventh century. This has been clearly stated in every case.

3. Manuscripts written in Ireland or on the European Continent (including Brittany) if they certainly or very probably found their way to England by 1100. Doubtful cases are clearly marked.

A manuscript in these three categories is included whether or not it was exported or re-exported from England and, if it was, irrespective of whether this occurred during the Anglo-Saxon period or later.

The following have been excluded:

1. Single-leaf documents. For such manuscripts, covering the period up to 1066, see P. H. Sawyer, *Anglo-Saxon Charters. An Annotated List and Bibliography* (London, 1968).[21]

2. Manuscripts that were written, or annotated, or decorated by Anglo-Saxon scribes and artists on the Continent but that are not known to have been in England at any time before 1100. Doubtful cases are clearly marked.

3. Manuscripts in Anglo-Saxon scripts written by English or by continental scribes, (trained and) working at Anglo-Saxon centres on the Continent.

4. Continental manuscripts presumably lent for copying in Anglo-Saxon England and afterwards returned, when there is no certain evidence for the sojourn of such a book in England.[22]

Two doubtful areas need to be mentioned. The first concerns eighth-century manuscripts, mainly in insular script, written, according to expert opinion (E. A. Lowe, *Codices Latini Antiquiores*), 'presumably' in England, or either in England or an Anglo-Saxon centre on the Continent. I have included some thirty of these manuscripts which are now thought to have possibly or probably originated in an English scriptorium. Here I was able to consult Bernhard Bischoff – whose important share in *CLA* is well-known – who considered more than twenty books in this category as certainly or probably English.[23]

A related problem is posed by early Continental or Irish manuscripts that may have reached the Anglo-Saxon missionaries in Germany either via England or more directly from Italy or Ireland; of these I have included nos. 799, 827.6 and 827.7. A further group of early manuscripts that could not be ignored are those that are thought to have been written either in Ireland or in England (probably Northumbria). They are represented by nos. 213, 214, 218, 664.5, 773.3, 893 and 929 in the *Handlist*.

The other area, even more problematic as it turned out, are the manuscripts of the late eleventh century. The chosen cut-off date for the „Preliminary List", i. e. at 1100, may today seem unfortunate but appeared a practical solution at a time when there were still many manuscripts that had simply been dated 's. xi'. Above all, it seemed important to remember that Anglo-Saxon literary, textual and scribal traditions had not come to a sudden stop in 1066 or, say, in 1070; one need only consider the twelfth-century manuscripts described in Neil Ker's *Catalogue of Manuscripts Containing Anglo-Saxon*.

But the drawback and pitfalls involved in this cut-off date are also obvious: of not a few manuscripts it was uncertain if they had in fact been written by 1100; books written by Norman scribes might have been produced in Normandy or in England, and, if written in France, it was uncertain if they had reached England by 1100. Also, not a few of these books were representative of what I have called the Norman library programme in England, containing texts, particularly patristic works, that had not been available previously in Anglo-Saxon England, or for that matter in the late Anglo-Saxon period, a programme that is particularly well-documented today in surviving manuscripts from some of the cathedrals and cathedral priories (Canterbury, Durham, Exeter and Salisbury). Teresa Webber's excellent work, mentioned above, convincingly demonstrates the issue.

In the meantime, however, much light has been thrown on this important period in the history of libraries and book-production in England. As so often, Neil Ker paved the way[24], and the work by Richard Gameson, Michael Gullick and Teresa Webber has helped to provide a thorough assessment of the evidence.[25] It may have seemed time, therefore, to drop all items dated s. xi ex. or later from the *Handlist*, but as Gameson's *The Manuscripts of Early Norman England (c. 1066 – 1130)* only came into my hands after the *Handlist* was finished, I decided to retain the late eleventh-century manuscripts for the time being; also, the respective entries may help to demonstrate the momentous changes in English book-production and library holdings in the later eleventh century. Manuscripts dated s. xi ex. or xi/xii will, however, no longer be included in the projected „Bibliographical Handlist of Anglo-Saxon Manuscripts".

As a result, it seems important to warn readers that items in the *Handlist* may contain texts that were not actually known or available in Anglo-Saxon England, or at least in the period from King Alfred to Edward the Confessor and William the Conqueror. I have, however, made every effort to delete items originally included in the „Preliminary List" if they cannot be shown to have been written in England, or to have reached the country, by 1100; all doubtful cases have been clearly marked.

The following items recorded in the „Preliminary List" have been excluded because palaeographers are now agreed that they should be dated after 1100:
47, 49, 71, 84, 89, 94, 160, 183, 187, 197, 198, 201, 203, 305, 318, 335, 420, 495, 504, 562, 579, 588, 624, 634, 645, 683, 698, 701, 705, 708, 709, 718, 719, 721, 723, 726, 727, 731, 732, 737, 746, 747, 826.
These serial numbers are now vacant and, in order to avoid confusion, have not been re-used.

A small number of items have been deleted because they record manuscripts written on the Continent, mainly datable s. xi ex. or s. xi/xii, which are unlikely to have reached England by 1100: nos. 10, 33, 113, 205, 687 and 797 of the „Preliminary List". Where arrival of a book in England by the end of the eleventh century is probable, but not certain, this has been duly noted at the end of the respective entry.

Lost, destroyed and untraced manuscripts and fragments have been recorded under their former owners; it is to be hoped that at least some of them may turn up again one day. See nos. 643, 830.5, 831.4, 842.5 (formerly no. 943), 855.5, and the *membra disiecta* listed under nos. 176 and 441.1. For lost copies of manuscripts containing Old English texts or glosses, see also Ker, *Catalogue of Manuscripts Containing Anglo-Saxon*, nos. 403-412.

Item no. 78 remains vacant, as in the „Preliminary List"; no. 679 has been cancelled; this was based on unreliable information, apparently referring to no. 692.5.

Serial numbers

The *Handlist* is ordered according to the location of the manuscripts in modern libraries. There are two alphabetical sequences, one of libraries in the British Isles and the other of libraries on the European Continent, in the U.S.A., Japan and New Zealand. This division may not seem ideal, but had to be taken over from the „Preliminary List" in order not to disturb the numbering sequence.

Membra disiecta of an originally single manuscript are not separately numbered but are treated together as one item. The 'group item' is normally placed in the list where the main component belongs, if there is one, or, if there is no main one, where the first component occurs. The other component(s) are specified in the group item in the order which they have in the list. A cross-reference to the group item is supplied at the point(s) in the list at which the other component(s) occur.

The serial numbers of the „Preliminary List" have been retained. New entries are indicated by a decimal point and figure. Newly found *membra disiecta* of known items have been recorded but, in accordance with previous practice (see above), have not been given a serial number of their own. Separate serial numbers for parts of manuscripts now bound as one volume have been allocated only when it seemed unlikely that these parts had been together before 1100, but absolute consistency in such cases may not have been attained. Serial numbers of deleted items (see above) have in no case been re-used.

The following manuscripts have been assigned new serial numbers because of a change of ownership or of a permanent loan:

„Preliminary List" no.	623	now *Handlist* no.	754.6
	625		754.5
	695		212.2
	756		501.2
	817		848.8
	935		849.3

Cross-references have been provided for all six items. The previous serial numbers remain vacant. For other numbers now vacant, see above.

Since the city of Leningrad was renamed, it might have been proper to move nos. 840.5-847 in the Russian National Library to a position after no. 933.5, but it has seemed advisable to me to keep these ten important manuscripts where they were and, instead, to provide a cross-reference.

Shelf-marks

Changes occur only in a few cases where manuscripts or fragments were assigned different shelf-marks or where a shelf-mark was assigned for the first time (previously „s. n."). In the former case, the old shelf-marks are always noted at the end of the respective entries.[26] For change of ownership, see above.

Contents of Manuscripts

In the „Preliminary List", only the main items in each manuscript could be recorded. In the *Handlist*, an attempt has now been made to list the contents of manuscripts and fragments as fully as possible. It is important to remember, however, that the relatively brief entries cannot serve as substitutes for detailed descriptions; thus it is clear that the *Handlist* cannot do full justice to such complex books as the copies of Wulfstan's „Handbook"[27] or to the widely varying contents of liturgical books. It has therefore seemed advisable to include references to full descriptions or editions of such books where they are available, marked „FC:" (full

9

contents) at the end of entries. A list of abbreviations or abbreviated titles used for this purpose will be found following this Introduction. No such references are given for manuscripts with contents wholly or mainly in Old English, as their detailed descriptions can conveniently be found in Neil Ker's *Catalogue of Manuscripts Containing Anglo-Saxon.*

The following details have not normally been recorded:

Minor additions and alterations

Scattered glosses in Latin or Old English

Supply leaves[28]

Additions of any kind, and glosses (English, French or Latin) entered after 1100

Introductory texts to biblical books, and 'argumenta' preceding the psalms in some psalter manuscripts

Canon tables, lists of capitula, and explanations of Hebrew names in Gospel books[29]

Lists of *capitula* in texts like the Rules of St. Benedict and Chrodegang, Penitentials, etc.

Illustrations and decoration[30]

Musical notation.[31]

'Cantica' in psalter manuscripts often include not only the eleven biblical canticles of the Office, but also *Te Deum, Gloria, Pater noster,* the Apostles' Creed (*Credo*) and the Athanasian Creed (*Quicumque vult*); these have not been separately listed.[32]

Identification of texts and authors: Readers will have no difficulty in identifying texts in Old English, anonymous or by known authors, and texts with Old English glosses, recorded in the entries of the *Handlist* by consulting Ker's *Catalogue* and the „List of Old English Texts" by Angus Cameron;[33] however, a considerable number of editions of texts more recent than those listed by Ker and Cameron are now available and can be found listed in the standard bibliographies.

A large proportion of the Latin texts can be identified in the standard handbooks, especially the *Clavis Patrum Latinorum* and the histories of Medieval Latin literature by Manitius and Brunhölzl.[34] But there are a considerable number of problematic texts, such as

10

anonymous and pseudonymous homilies and letters, for which a comprehensive study and index is badly needed.[35] Also, „Computus material" in the entries refers to a class of widely varying texts and tables. I regret that it has not been possible to specify these in detail when they occur. It is to be hoped that an expert in the field will one day produce a repertory of such materials in Anglo-Saxon manuscripts.[36]

I have tried, however, to provide identifying references for two categories of texts:

1.   For Saints' lives that could be identified, referring readers to the *Bibliotheca Hagiographica Latina* („*BHL*");[37] but for collections of such Lives see the references under nos. 36, 344, 898.

2.   For shorter, mainly anonymous Latin poems. References are to the inventory of Schaller and Könsgen, wherever possible („SK"), and only in a few cases to Walther's *Initia* („W") or the *Analecta Hymnica* („*AH*").[38] But it is important to remember that for quite a number of texts more recent editions than those listed in these handbooks have become available in the meantime. Again, no such references are supplied for large collections of Latin secular or religious poetry, like the 'Cambridge Songs' (in no. 12), the hymnals, and tropers with sequences. For these, see the references preceded by „FC" in the individual entries. Readers will note that an appreciable number of Latin poems (including liturgical compositions) extant in Anglo-Saxon manuscripts are not recorded in Schaller-Könsgen or Walther, nor in the six volumes of Ulysse Chevalier, *Repertorium Hymnologicum* (1892-1921); the manuscripts containing such poems are listed in Index II D.

For the contents, the following symbols have been employed, as in the „Preliminary List":

(no symbol)	text in Latin
*	text in Old English
(*)	text partly in Old English
+*	text in Latin, accompanied by a prose version in Old English; or a Latin-Old English glossary
°	Latin text with continuous Old English interlinear gloss, or having substantial sections, or a fairly large number of words, glossed in Old English
(f)	only minor fragments of a text are preserved.

For texts in languages other than Latin or Old English, the language is specified in the entries. In the case of translations into Latin or Old English, the translator's name, if known, follows in round brackets the name of the author.

Dates

All dates given towards the end of each entry (after a colon) refer to the main items. Where texts have been added later, their date is usually indicated in round brackets, immediately following the respective title. The opinion of expert palaeographers in their most recent publications has always been followed. The accuracy and specificity of dating a book or fragment depend on different kinds of evidence in each individual case: what is known about the history of a manuscript, about the scriptorium where it was written, its contents and, above all, its handwriting. Dates given may therefore be more or less specific and narrow, sometimes even uncertain. As a consequence, the form of dates in the *Handlist* does not follow a consistent system, the aim being to provide a date as precise as is at present possible for each item. Where experts differ, this has been taken into account by listing the two or sometimes three suggested dates, always linked by „or".

Origin and Provenance

Care has been taken to distinguish clearly between origin and provenance of a manuscript, as far as these are known. Dates for pre-1100 provenance have been given if possible. The following conventions have been used:

place-name (unmarked)	:	place of origin
„prov." + place-name	:	provenance before 1100
(„prov." + place-name)	:	provenance after 1100

Where the place of origin and/or provenance of a manuscript is probable or uncertain, this has been indicated by „prob." or by a question-mark. The places of provenance, if more than one is known, are listed in chronological order. Where no place or region of origin is given it is to be assumed that the manuscript in question originated in England.

The known places of origin or provenance in Anglo-Saxon England are almost exclusively cathedrals, cathedral priories and Benedictine abbeys and nunneries.[39] For the houses in Canterbury and Winchester, the following abbreviations have been used:

CC   Christ Church, Canterbury

StA   St. Augustine's, Canterbury

NM   New Minster, Winchester

Nun   Nunnaminster, Winchester

OM   Old Minster, Winchester

Acknowledgements

To attempt a thorough revision of the „Preliminary List" and to produce a *Handlist of Anglo-Saxon Manuscripts* would have been impossible without the active support of friends, colleagues and librarians all over the world, and of some private owners of manuscripts. For providing me with information about newly-found books and fragments, for suggesting addenda, corrigenda and various kinds of improvement and for patiently answering my enquiries I am deeply grateful to Maria Amalia d'Aronco, Bruce Barker-Benfield, Carl T. Berkhout, Walter Berschin, Mary Catherine Bodden, Michelle P. Brown, Mildred Budny, Donald Bullough, James P. Carley, Jimmy Cross, Ian Doyle, Elaine M. Drage, Allen Frantzen, David Ganz, Lilli Gjerløw, Timothy Graham, Christopher Hohler, Peter Jackson, Colette Jeudy, Sarah Larratt Keefer, Matti Kilpiö, Patrizia Lendinara, Rosamond McKitterick, Paul Meyvaert, Jennifer Morrish Tunberg, Thomas H. Ohlgren, R. I. Page, Susan Rankin, Frank A. Rella, Pamela Robinson, William P. Stoneman, Paul E. Szarmach, Rodney Thomson, Jean Vezin, Linda E. Voigts, Gernot Wieland and Joseph Wittig. I also wish to thank the numerous librarians, especially in Cambridge, London and Oxford, who helped to make my work rewarding and enjoyable, and Mr Martin Schøyen and Professor Toshiyuki Takamiya, who sent me information about manuscripts recently acquired by them.

Here in Munich, in the Department of English young colleagues, research assistants and Ph. D. candidates have for many years supported my project by bibliographical work, computerizing draft versions of the *Handlist*, and by sharing the results of their own work with me: Birgit Ebersperger, Helene Feulner, Mechthild Gretsch, Ursula Kalbhen, Gabriele Knappe, Michael Korhammer, Lucia Kornexl, Ursula Lenker, Hans Sauer, Carolin Schreiber, Wolfhard Steppe, Roland Torkar, Karl Toth and Svenja Weidinger. The *Handlist* could not have been printed without the work and assistance of Rebecca Rushforth of Trinity College, Cambridge, who expertly (and patiently) produced computer versions of List and Introduction, who skilfully turned my handwritten Indexes into such versions, and who saved me from quite a number of errors and inconsistencies. At the final stage of preparing the book for publication, the assistance and advice by Birgit Ebersperger of the Bayerische Akademie der Wissenschaften have been invaluable.

I owe special thanks to four colleagues who systematically went through a draft version of the *Handlist* and let me have extensive comments: David Dumville, Simon Keynes, Drew Hartzell (all three having regularly sent valuable information for many years before), and Teresa Webber. I also appreciate the great kindness of Richard Gameson, who let me see two draft versions of his important catalogue of the manuscripts of Early Norman England. At a late stage in my work I met Michael Gullick; it is difficult to put in words how much I owe to his thorough analysis of the *Handlist* (as it was in late 1997), and to the unselfish way in which he shared his expert knowledge, particularly of late Anglo-Saxon and early Norman books. I owe my knowledge of a considerable number of late eleventh-century manuscripts to Richard Gameson and Michael Gullick.

Once again I should like to express my gratitude to the palaeographers whose advice was essential for the preparation of the „Preliminary List", and who continued with advice and information after it was published, especially Neil Ker and T. A. M. Bishop, also Julian Brown and Malcolm Parkes. In Munich, Bernhard Bischoff never failed to answer my queries immediately, and until shortly before his death he kept passing on to me notes on Anglo-Saxon work that he had found in the course of preparing his catalogue of ninth-century manuscripts.

Finally, I must name the two friends and scholars without whose encouragement, advice and support neither the „Preliminary List" nor this *Handlist* would have been prepared and published: Peter Clemoes, who sadly cannot see and judge this new version of what he first ventured to have printed, and Michael Lapidge, whose unrivalled scholarship and energetic help has contributed more to the *Handlist* than I can express in a few words.

I am well aware that what I have to offer in this *Handlist* is still far from perfect and complete; as a consequence, I am inclined to see it as just another search-list, and I shall be most grateful for any information on possible gaps and errors, and for suggestions for improvement. Those who feel that a *Handlist of Anglo-Saxon Manuscripts* should not yet have been published in this form and at this stage may take some comfort in reading what Henry Sweet, a hundred years ago, had to say about 'good' and 'bad' dictionaries on p. v of his admirable *Student's*

Dictionary of Anglo-Saxon (Oxford, 1896). My main effort will now be devoted to the preparation of a „Bibliographical Handlist of Anglo-Saxon Manuscripts", recording all essential publications (palaeographical and codicological work, editions, facsimiles, reproductions etc.) on each of the manuscripts in the *Handlist*.

H. G.

NOTES

[1] George Hickes, „Catalogus Veterum Librorum Septentrionalium", in *Institutiones Grammaticae Anglo-Saxonicae et Moeso-Gothicae* (Oxford, 1689); cf. Helmut Gneuss, „Der älteste Katalog der angelsächsischen Handschriften und seine Nachfolger", in Gneuss, *Books and Libraries in Early England* (Aldershot, 1996), no. X; Humfrey Wanley, *Antiquae Literaturae Septentrionalis Liber Alter seu Humphredi Wanleii Librorum Vett. Septentrionalium ... Catalogus Historico-Criticus* (Oxford, 1705); N. R. Ker, *Catalogue of Manuscripts Containing Anglo-Saxon* (Oxford, 1957); Supplement by Ker in *Anglo-Saxon England*, 5 (1976), 121-131; addenda and corrigenda to the Supplement by Mary Blockley in *Anglo-Saxon Manuscripts: Basic Readings*, ed. Mary P. Richards (New York, 1994), pp. 79-85.

[2] Helmut Gneuss, „Liturgical Books in Anglo-Saxon England and their Old English Terminology", in *Books and Libraries in Early England*, no. V (orig. publ. 1985).

[3] J. D. A. Ogilvy, *Books Known to the English, 597-1066* (Cambridge, MA, 1967); cf. review by Helmut Gneuss, *Anglia*, 89 (1971), 129-134, utilized in Ogilvy, „Books Known to the English, A. D. 597-1066: *Addenda et Corrigenda*", *Mediaevalia*, 7 (1984 for 1981), 281-325 [repr. as vol. 11 of Old English Newsletter Subsidia (Binghamton, NY, 1985)]. Earlier version: *Books Known to Anglo-Latin Writers from Aldhelm to Alcuin* (Cambridge, MA, 1936); review by Bernhard Bischoff, *Historisches Jahrbuch*, 57 (1937), 125-127.

[4] Helmut Gneuss, „A preliminary list of manuscripts written or owned in England up to 1100", *Anglo-Saxon England*, 9 (1981), 1-60.

[5] Ker (see note 1); T. A. M. Bishop, *English Caroline Minuscule* (Oxford, 1971) and his articles listed *ibid.*, p. xxvii; J. J. G. Alexander, *Insular Manuscripts 6th to the 9th century* (London, 1978); Elzbieta Temple, *Anglo-Saxon Manuscripts 900-1066* (London, 1976); E. A. Lowe, *Codices Latini Antiquiores*, 11 vols. and Suppl. (Oxford, 1934-71, vol. II sec. ed. 1972). Two articles by Bernhard Bischoff, Virginia Brown and James J. John listing and describing addenda to *CLA* have appeared in *Medieval Studies*, 47 (1985), 317-366 and 54 (1992), 286-307. A further supplement is in preparation.

[6] Only some of the most important publications can here be recorded: Rodney M. Thomson, *Catalogue of the Manuscripts of Lincoln Cathedral Chapter Library* (Woodbridge, 1989); R. A. B. Mynors and R. M. Thomson, *Catalogue of the Manuscripts in Hereford Cathedral Library*

(Cambridge, 1993); N. R. Ker, *Medieval Manuscripts in British Libraries*, 4 vols. [vol. IV with A. J. Piper] (Oxford, 1969-92); A. G. Watson, *Catalogue of Dated and Datable Manuscripts c. 700-1600 in the Department of Manuscripts, The British Library* (London, 1979); *id.*, *Catalogue of Dated and Datable Manuscripts c. 435-1600 in Oxford Libraries* (Oxford, 1984); P. R. Robinson, *Catalogue of Dated and Datable Manuscripts c. 737-1600 in Cambridge Libraries* (Cambridge, 1988); *The Golden Age of Anglo-Saxon Art 966-1066*, ed. Janet Backhouse, D. H. Turner, Leslie Webster (London, 1984); *The Making of England: Anglo-Saxon Art and Culture AD 600-900*, ed. Leslie Webster and Janet Backhouse (London, 1991); *Early English Manuscripts in Facsimile*, various editors, I- (Copenhagen, 1951-); *Anglo-Saxon Manuscripts in Microfiche Facsimile*, ed. A. N. Doane and Ph. Pulsiano, 1- (Binghamton, 1994-). For numerous further, pertinent publications see the annual bibliographies in *Scriptorium, Anglo-Saxon England* and *Old English Newsletter*. See also note 5, above.

[7] See especially David Dumville, *English Caroline Script and Monastic History: Studies in Benedictinism, A. D. 950-1030* (Woodbridge, 1993); *id.*, „English Square minuscule script: the background and earliest phases", *Anglo-Saxon England*, 16 (1987), 147-179; *id.*, „English Square minuscule script: the mid-century phases", *Anglo-Saxon England*, 23 (1994), 133-164; Simon Keynes, „King Athelstan's Books", in *Learning and Literature in Anglo-Saxon England. Studies presented to Peter Clemoes*, ed. Michael Lapidge and Helmut Gneuss (Cambridge, 1985), pp. 143-201, *id.*, *The Liber Vitae of the New Minster and Hyde Abbey Winchester*, Early English Manuscripts in Facsimile 26 (Copenhagen, 1996); Michael Lapidge, *Anglo-Latin Literature 600-899* (London, 1996), *id.*, *Anglo-Latin Literature 900-1066* (London, 1993).

[8] Helmut Gneuss, „A newly-found fragment of an Anglo-Saxon psalter", *Anglo-Saxon England*, 27 (1998), 273-287.

[9] The 'Anderson Pontifical', written c. 1000 or early in the eleventh century at Christ Church, Canterbury (or the Old Minster, Winchester?) and acquired by the British Library in 1971; now MS B.L. Add. 57337. For a reproduction of fol. 103 see Andrew Prescott, „The Structure of English Pre-Conquest Benedictionals", *British Library Journal*, 13 (1987), 118-158, at p. 122.

[10] Teresa Webber, *Scribes and Scholars at Salisbury Cathedral c. 1075 – c. 1125* (Oxford, 1992); Birgit Ebersperger, *Die angelsächsischen Handschriften in den Pariser Bibliotheken*, Anglistische Forschungen 261 (Heidelberg, 1999).

17

[11] Admirably edited and annotated by Michael Lapidge, „Surviving booklists from Anglo-Saxon England", in *Anglo-Saxon Manuscripts: Basic Readings* (see note 1), pp. 87-167, rev. repr. of article in *Learning and Literature in Anglo-Saxon England. Studies Presented to Peter Clemoes*, ed. M. Lapidge and H. Gneuss (Cambridge, 1985), pp. 33-89.

[12] See N. R. Ker, *Medieval Libraries of Great Britain: A List of Surviving Books*, second ed. (London, 1964), and *Supplement to the Second Edition*, ed. Andrew G. Watson (London, 1987).

[13] See Peter Jackson, „Fontes Anglo-Saxonici. A Register of Written Sources Used by Authors in Anglo-Saxon England. Fifteenth Progress Report", *Old English Newsletter*, 33, no. 3 (Spring 2000), 7-9; Rohini Jayatilaka, „*Fontes Anglo-Saxonici* on the World Wide Web", *Medieval English Studies Newsletter*, no. 41 (December 1999), 11-39; *Sources of Anglo-Saxon Literary Culture: A Trial Version*, ed. Frederick M. Biggs, Thomas D. Hill, Paul E. Szarmach (Binghamton, NY, 1990).

[14] For these manuscripts see Jennifer Morrish, „Dated and Datable Manuscripts Copied in England during the Ninth Century", *Mediaeval Studies*, 50 (1988), 512-538, and for the background the important article by Michael Lapidge, „Latin Learning in Ninth-Century England", in *Anglo-Latin Literature 600-899* (London, 1996), pp. 409-454.

[15] Helmut Gneuss, „King Alfred and the History of Anglo-Saxon Libraries", in *Books and Libraries in Early England*, no. III; also, „Anglo-Saxon Libraries from the Conversion to the Benedictine Reform", *ibid.*, no. II, pp. 672-676.

[16] Alfred's „Preface", ed. Dorothy Whitelock in *Sweet's Anglo-Saxon Reader in Prose and Verse* (Oxford, 1967), pp. 5-6. Italics are mine.
'When I reflected on all this, I recollected how – before everything was ransacked and burned – the churches throughout England stood filled with treasures and books. Similarly, there was a great multitude of those serving God. And they derived little benefit from those books, because they could understand nothing of them, since they were not written in their own language.' *Alfred the Great. Asser's Life of King Alfred and other contemporary sources*, trans., with Introduction and Notes by Simon Keynes and Michael Lapidge (Harmondsworth, 1983), p. 125.

[17] Bernhard Bischoff, *Katalog der festländischen Handschriften des neunten Jahrhunderts (mit Ausnahme der wisigotischen). Teil I: Aachen-Lambach* (Wiesbaden, 1998). Part II, Laon-Paderborn, is in preparation.

[18] N. R. Ker, *English Manuscripts in the Century after the Norman Conquest* (Oxford, 1960), pp. 7-8; Bishop, *English Caroline Minuscule*, pp. xvii-xviii. See also, for an even more critical assessment, Rodney M. Thomson, „The Norman Conquest and English Libraries", in *The Role of the Book in Medieval Culture*, ed. Peter Ganz, 2 vols. (Turnhout, 1896), II. 27-40. A more balanced view has now been convincingly proposed by Teresa Webber, „The Patristic Content of English Book Collections in the Eleventh Century: Towards a Continental Perspective", in *Of the Making of Books. Medieval Manuscripts, their Scribes and Readers. Essays presented to M. B. Parkes*, ed. P. R. Robinson and Rivkah Zim (Aldershot, 1997), pp. 191-205.

[19] Quoted from Inge B. Milfull, *The Hymns of the Anglo-Saxon Church*. Cambridge Studies in Anglo-Saxon England 17 (Cambridge, 1996), p. 386, no. 116.

[20] For a comprehensive inventory of what is preserved in Old English, see Angus Cameron, „A List of Old English Texts", in *A Plan for the Dictionary of Old English*, ed. Roberta Frank and A. Cameron (Toronto, 1973), pp. 25-306; see also Gneuss, „Anglo-Saxon Libraries" (as note 15), pp. 682-683.

[21] For recent work on these charters, and for facsimile editions, see Simon Keynes, *Anglo-Saxon England: A Bibliographical Handbook for Students of Anglo-Saxon History* (Cambridge, October 2000), pp. 32-34.

[22] For an example see Dumville, *English Caroline Script*, pp. 54-55, note 240.

[23] These are nos. 281.5, 791.3, 791.6, 791.9, 799.5, 804.5, 808.3, 808.5, 818.5, 830.5, 831.6, 831.7, 836.5, 840.5, 840.6, 848.6, 848.7, 855.5, 933.5, 943.4, 944.5, 946.5.

[24] *English Manuscripts in the Century after the Norman Conquest*; see note 18, above.

[25] See especially: Richard Gameson, „English Manuscript Art in the late Eleventh Century: Canterbury and its Context", in *Canterbury and the Norman Conquest. Churches, Saints and Scholars 1066 – 1109*, ed. Richard Eales and Richard Sharpe (London, 1995), pp. 95-144; Teresa Webber, „Script and Manuscript Production at Christ Church, Canterbury, after the Norman Conquest", *ibid.*, pp. 145-158 and, of course, her book referred to above and in note 10; Michael Gullick, „The Scribe of the Carilef Bible: A New Look at some Late-Eleventh-Century Durham Cathedral Manuscripts", in Linda Brownrigg, ed., *Medieval Book Production: Assessing the Evidence* (Los Altos Hills, CA, 1990), pp. 61-83; *id.*, „The Scribes of the Durham Cantor's Book (Durham, Dean and Chapter Library, MS B.IV.24) and the Durham Martyrology Scribe", in *Anglo-Norman Durham 1093-1193*, ed. David Rollason, Margaret Harvey, Michael

19

Prestwick (Woodbridge, 1994), pp. 93-109. I state in the Acknowledgements, below, what I owe to these three scholars. To the brief list in this footnote should now be added: Richard Gameson, *The Manuscripts of Early Norman England (c. 1066-1130)*, A British Academy Postdoctoral Fellowship Monograph (Oxford, 1999); for all manuscripts dated s. xi ex. or later in the *Handlist*, readers are advised also to consult this important book.

[26] Some great international authority (UN, EU?) could perform a meritorious service by passing legislation preventing librarians from changing the shelfmarks of manuscripts.

[27] For these, see Hans Sauer, „Zur Überlieferung und Analyse von Erzbischof Wulfstans 'Handbuch' ", *Deutsches Archiv für Erforschung des Mittelalters*, 36 (1980), 341-384; Mildred Budny, *Insular, Anglo-Saxon, and Early Anglo-Norman Manuscript Art at Corpus Christi College, Cambridge* (Kalamazoo, MI, 1997), especially I. 535-544 and 599-608; most recently, *Wulfstan's Canon Law Collection*, ed. J. E. Cross and Andrew Hamer, Anglo-Saxon Texts 1 (Cambridge, 1999).

[28] An important contribution to this field is by M. B. Parkes, „Archaizing Hands in English Manuscripts", in *Books and Collectors 1200 – 1700. Essays presented to Andrew Watson*, ed. James P. Carley and Colin G. C. Tite (London, 1997), pp. 101-141.

[29] But all lists of gospel pericopes, and pertinent pericope notes, have been duly recorded. Ursula Lenker has recently demonstrated their significance, and I have been able to rely on her pioneer work: *Die westsächsische Evangelienversion und die Perikopenordnungen im angelsächsischen England*. TUEPh 20 (München, 1997).

[30] Much work has been done in these fields. For comprehensive catalogues see Alexander and Temple (note 5, above); Thomas H. Ohlgren, *Insular and Anglo-Saxon Illuminated Manuscripts: An Iconographic Catalogue c. A. D. 625 to 1100* (New York, 1986); a revised computerized version has appeared.

[31] Catalogues and studies of Anglo-Saxon manuscripts with musical notation are in preparation by Professor K. D. Hartzell and by Dr Susan Rankin. See also the literature quoted by Milfull, *The Hymns of the Anglo-Saxon Church*, notes to pp. 92-95.

[32] For an index to these texts in Anglo-Saxon psalter manuscripts, see Phillip Pulsiano, „Psalters", in *The Liturgical Books of Anglo-Saxon England*, ed. Richard W. Pfaff. Old English Newsletter Subsidia 23 (Kalamazoo, MI, 1995), pp. 80-83.

[33] See notes 1 and 20, above.

[34]   Eligius Dekkers and Aemilius Gaar, *Clavis Patrum Latinorum*, third ed. (Steenbrugge, 1995); Max Manitius, *Geschichte der lateinischen Literatur des Mittelalters*, 3 vols. (München, 1911-1931); Franz Brunhölzl, *Geschichte der lateinischen Literatur des Mittelalters*, 2 vols. (München, 1975-1992). Other essential reference works are: Michael Lapidge and Richard Sharpe, *A Bibliography of Celtic-Latin Literature 400 – 1200* (Dublin, 1985); Richard Sharpe, *A Handlist of the Latin Writers of Great Britain and Ireland before 1540*. Publications of the Journal of Medieval Latin 1 (Turnhout, 1997); *Clavis Scriptorum Latinorum Medii Aevi: Auctores Galliae, 735 – 987*, ed. Marie-Hélène Jullien and Françoise Perelman, I- (Turnhout, 1994-).

[35]   An important, recently published research tool in this field is: Johannes Machielsen, *Clavis Patristica Pseudepigraphorum Medii Aevi*. I: *Opera Homiletica*, 2 vols. (Turnhout, 1990); II: *Theologica, Exegetica, Ascetica, Monastica*, 2 vols. (Turnhout, 1994).

[36]   For important recent work in this field, see *Byrhtferth's Enchiridion*, ed. Peter S. Baker and Michael Lapidge. EETS S.S.15 (Oxford, 1995), especially pp. xxxiv-lx, from where I take my references to certain types of computus ('Winchester' computus, etc.); *Ælfwine's Prayerbook (London, British Library, Cotton Titus D.xxvi + xxvii)*, ed. Beate Günzel. Henry Bradshaw Society 108 (London, 1993); also Peter S. Baker, „Computus", in *The Blackwell Encyclopaedia of Anglo-Saxon England*, ed. Michael Lapidge, John Blair, Simon Keynes and Donald Scragg (Oxford, 1999), pp. 119-120.

[37]   For *BHL*, see the list of abbreviated references, below.

[38]   For the abbreviated references, see the list below. Where a poem is recorded by both Schaller-Könsgen and Walther, only the Schaller-Könsgen number is given in the *Handlist*.

[39]   For the dioceses and bishops' seats in Anglo-Saxon England, see Simon Keynes, „Episcopal Succession in Anglo-Saxon England", in *Handbook of British Chronology*, ed. E. B. Fryde, D. E. Greenway, S. Porter and I. Roy, third ed. (London, 1986), pp. 209-224. For Anglo-Saxon abbeys and cathedral priories, see Keynes, *Anglo-Saxon History*, pp. 15-29; for those of the tenth and eleventh centuries, see also David Knowles and R. N. Hadcock, *Medieval Religious Houses: England and Wales*, second ed. (London, 1971), and David Knowles, C. N. L. Brooke and Vera C. M. London, *The Heads of Religious Houses: England and Wales 940 – 1216* (Cambridge, 1971).

Abbreviations and abbreviated references

AH	*Analecta Hymnica Medii Aevi*, ed. Guido Maria Dreves, Clemens Blume and Henry M. Bannister, 55 vols. (Leipzig, 1886-1922), quoted by volume and page.
ASE	*Anglo-Saxon England.*
ASM	*Anglo-Saxon Manuscripts in Microfiche Facsimile*, ed. A. N. Doane and Phillip Pulsiano, vols. 1-4 (Binghamton, NY, 1994-1996); vols. 5- (Tempe, AZ, 1997-).
Banting (1989)	*Two Anglo-Saxon Pontificals*, ed. H. M. J. Banting. HBS 104 (1989).
BHL	*Bibliotheca Hagiographica Latina*. Subsidia Hagiographica 6 (Brussels, 1898-99), and *Novum Supplementum*, ed. H. Fros. Subsidia Hagiographica 70 (Brussels, 1986).
Bischoff (1998)	Bernhard Bischoff, *Katalog der festländischen Handschriften des neunten Jahrhunderts. Teil I: Aachen – Lambach* (Wiesbaden, 1998).
Budny (1997)	Mildred Budny, *Insular, Anglo-Saxon, and Early Anglo-Norman Manuscript Art at Corpus Christi College, Cambridge. An Illustrated Catalogue*, 2 vols. (Kalamazoo, MI, 1997).
Colker (1991)	Marvin L. Colker, *Trinity College Library Dublin: Descriptive Catalogue of the Mediaeval and Renaissance Latin Manuscripts*, 2 vols. (Aldershot, 1991).
Cross and Hamer (1999)	*Wulfstan's Canon Law Collection*, ed. J. E. Cross and Andrew Hamer. Anglo-Saxon Texts 1 (Cambridge, 1999).
CSASE	Cambridge Studies in Anglo-Saxon England.
CUL Cat.	[Charles Hardwick and Henry L. Luard] *A Catalogue of the Manuscripts Preserved in the Library of the University of Cambridge*, 5 vols. (Cambridge, 1856-67).
Dewick and Frere (1914-21)	*The Leofric Collectar*, ed. Edward Samuel Dewick and Walter Howard Frere. HBS 45, 56 (1914-21).
EEMF	Early English Manuscripts in Facsimile.
Frere (1894)	*The Winchester Troper*, ed. Walter Howard Frere. HBS 8 (1894).

Gneuss (1968)	Helmut Gneuss, *Hymnar und Hymnen im englischen Mittelalter* (Tübingen, 1968).
HBS	Henry Bradshaw Society.
Jackson and Lapidge (1996)	Peter Jackson and Michael Lapidge, „The Contents of the Cotton-Corpus Legendary", in *Holy Men and Holy Women. Old English Prose Saints' Lives and their Contexts*, ed. Paul E. Szarmach (Albany, NY, 1996), pp. 131-146.
James (1905)	Montague Rhodes James, *A Descriptive Catalogue of the Manuscripts in the Library of Pembroke College* (Cambridge, 1905).
James and Jenkins (1932)	M. R. James and Claude Jenkins, *A Descriptive Catalogue of the Manuscripts in the Library of Lambeth Palace* (Cambridge, 1932).
Korhammer (1976)	Michael Korhammer, *Die monastischen Cantica im Mittelalter und ihre altenglischen Interlinearversionen.* TUEPh 6 (München, 1976).
Kuypers (1902)	A. B. Kuypers, *The Prayer Book of Aedeluald the Bishop, Commonly Called the Book of Cerne* (Cambridge, 1902).
Lapidge (1985)	Michael Lapidge, „Surviving Booklists from Anglo-Saxon England", in *Learning and Literature in Anglo-Saxon England. Studies Presented to Peter Clemoes*, ed. M. Lapidge and H. Gneuss (Cambridge, 1985), pp. 33-89; rev. repr. in *Anglo-Saxon Manuscripts: Basic Readings*, ed. Mary P. Richards (New York, 1994), pp. 87-167.
Loyn (1971)	*A Wulfstan Manuscript, Containing Institutes, Laws and Homilies. British Museum Cotton Nero A.I*, ed. Henry Loyn. EEMF 17 (Copenhagen, 1971).
MÆ	*Medium Ævum.*
Planchart (1977)	Alejandro Enrique Planchart, *The Repertory of Tropes at Winchester*, 2 vols. (Princeton, N.J., 1977).
Prescott (1988)	Andrew Prescott, „The Structure of English Pre-Conquest Benedictionals", *The British Library Journal*, 13 (1988), 118-158.
Richards (1988)	Mary P. Richards, *Texts and their Traditions in the Medieval Library of Rochester Cathedral Priory.* Transactions of the American Philosophical Society, 78 pt. 3 (Philadelphia, 1988).

Rud (1825)	Thomas Rud, *Codicum Manuscriptorum Ecclesiae Cathedralis Dunelmensis Catalogus Classicus* (Durham, 1825).
Sauer (2000)	Hans Sauer, „The Transmission and Structure of Archbishop Wulfstan's 'Commonplace Book'", in *Old English Prose. Basic Readings*, ed. Paul E. Szarmach (New York, 2000), 339-393.
Saxl and Meier (1953)	Fritz Saxl and Hans Meier, *Catalogue of Astrological and Mythological Manuscripts of the Latin Middle Ages III: Manuscripts in English Libraries*, ed. Harry Bober, 2 vols. (London, 1953).
Schenkl (1891-1908)	Heinrich Schenkl, *Bibliotheca Patrum Latinorum Britannica* (repr. Hildesheim, 1969). Originally published 1891-1908 in *Sitzungsberichte der philosophisch-historischen Classe der kaiserlichen Akademie der Wissenschaften* (Vienna).
SK	Dieter Schaller and Ewald Könsgen, *Initia carminum Latinorum saeculo undecimo antiquiorum. Bibliographisches Repertorium für die lateinische Dichtung der Antike und des früheren Mittelalters* (Göttingen, 1977).
Smith and Tite (1984)	Thomas Smith, *Catalogue of the Manuscripts in the Cottonian Library 1696*, ed. C. G. C. Tite (Cambridge, 1984).
TCBS	*Transactions of the Cambridge Bibliographical Society.*
TUEPh	Texte und Untersuchungen zur Englischen Philologie.
Turner (1971)	*The Claudius Pontificals*, ed. D. H. Turner. HBS 97 (1971).
W	Hans Walther, *Initia carminum ac versuum medii aevi posterioris Latinorum. Alphabetisches Verzeichnis der Versanfänge mittellateinischer Dichtungen*, second ed. (Göttingen, 1969).
Warner and Gilson (1921)	George F. Warner and Julius P. Gilson, *Catalogue of Western Manuscripts in the Old Royal and King's Collections*, 4 vols. (London, 1921).
Webber (1992)	Teresa Webber, *Scribes and Scholars at Salisbury Cathedral c. 1075 – c. 1125* (Oxford, 1992).

HANDLIST

I. LIBRARIES IN THE BRITISH ISLES

Aberdeen, University Library

1   216   Beda, *In Apocalypsin* ; Victorinus of Pettau (recension by Jerome), *In Apocalypsin* : s. xi ex., Salisbury.

Aberystwyth, National Library of Wales

1.5   735 C   fols. 1-26 : Bonifatius, *Aenigmata* ; Ausonius, Poem (opusc.VII.4; SK 4582) ; Astronomical drawings ; (Pseudo?-)Sallust and Pseudo-Cicero, *Invectivae* ; Cicero, *Somnium Scipionis* ; Macrobius, *In Somnium Scipionis* (f) ; Germanicus, *Aratea* : s. xi[1], France (Limoges?), prov. England or Wales, s. xi.
fols. 27-47 : Hyginus, *Astronomica* : s. xi, England or Wales.

Badminton, Gloucestershire, Duke of Beaufort Muniments

2   704.1.16   Venantius Fortunatus, *Carmina*, bk.V, Praefatio (f) : s. $x^{3/4}$, Canterbury?

Brockenhurst, Hampshire, Parish Church

2.2   Parish Register   Cassiodorus (ed.), *Historia tripartita* (f) : s. $ix^{2/4}$, NE France.

Cambridge, University Library

2.5   Dd.2.7   Jerome and Pseudo-Jerome, *Epistolae* : s. xi ex., Canterbury CC.

2.8   Ee.1.23, fols. 1-69   Paschasius Radbertus, *De assumptione B.M.V.* ; Ephraem Syrus (in Latin), Six sermons : s. xi/xii.

3   Ee.2.4   [with Oxford, Bodleian Library, Lat.th.c.3, fols. 1, 1* and 2] Smaragdus, *Expositio in Regulam S. Benedicti* : s. x med., W or SW England? (Glastonbury?).

4   Ff.1.23   Prayers (add. s. xi med. or xi[2]) ; Psalterium Romanum° ; Canticles° ; Litany ; Prayers : s. x/xi or xi in. or $xi^{2/4}$ or xi med., Ramsey? Canterbury?

5   Ff.2.33, fols. i, ii, vi and vii   Concilium Africanum of A.D. 424 (f) : s. xi ex., Bury St. Edmunds.

6	Ff.3.9	Ezechiel (excerpt) ; Gregory, *Homiliae in Ezechielem* : s. xi ex., Canterbury CC.

7	Ff.4.42	Juvencus, *Libri Evangeliorum* (with Welsh, Irish and Latin glosses, s. x[1], and Latin glosses s. x/xi) ; Welsh verses (s. x[1]) ; Grammatical notes ; Hymn (SK 10920 ; s. x) ; Sequence ; Poems (partly illegible) : s. ix[2], Wales, prov. s. x/xi W England.

8	Ff.4.43	Smaragdus, *Diadema monachorum* : s. x[4/4], Canterbury CC.

9	Ff.5.27, fol. i	Psalterium Romanum (f) : s. vii/viii, Wearmouth-J.

11	Gg.3.28	Ælfric, *Catholic Homilies* (First and Second Series)*, *De temporibus anni** ; Prayers* ; Ælfric, *De Paenitentia**, Pastoral Letter I* (incomplete) : s. x/xi, Cerne?, (prov. Durham).

11.5	Gg.4.15, fols. 1-108	Beda, *In Epistolas Catholicas* : s. xi/xii, (prov. Eynsham).

11.8	Gg.4.28	Jerome, *In Prophetas minores* (Osee, Amos, Jonas, Abdias, Micha, Nahum) ; Account of a *libellus* by Athanasius : s. xi/xii.

12	Gg.5.35	Juvencus, *Libri Evangeliorum*, with glosses ; Sedulius, *Carmen Paschale* (with glosses from commentary by Remigius), Hymns ; Poems on Sedulius (SK 15784, 14842, 14841) ; Arator, *Historia apostolica*, with glosses ; Poems on Arator (SK 17136, 177) ; Prosper, *Epigrammata*, preceded by prefatory poem (SK 5836), *Versus ad coniugem* ; Prudentius, *Psychomachia* (with glosses), *Dittochaeon* ; Lactantius, *De phoenice* ; Boethius, *De consolatione Philosophiae*, with commentary by Remigius ; Hrabanus Maurus, *De laudibus s. crucis* ; Hucbald of Saint-Amand, *De harmonica institutione* ; Aldhelm, *De virginitate* (verse) ; Milo, *Carmen de sobrietate* ; Lapidary poem (SK 2326; by Frithegod?) ; Latin hymns and poems (SK 1409a [by Wulfstan cantor?], 10856 [from Prudentius, *Hamartigenia* 931-66], 11339, 12765, 12551 [*Heptametron de primordio mundi*, by Eugenius of Toledo?], 14640, 6687, 10204, 2086a, 16284, 14633, 10904, 2593, 16044) ; Abbo of Saint-Germain, *Bella Parisiacae urbis*, bk.iii ; Hucbald of Saint-Amand, *Ecloga de calvis* ; Eusebius, Tatwine, Bonifatius, Symphosius and (glossed) Aldhelm, *Aenigmata* ; Pseudo-Smaragdus (Pseudo-Alcuin), Two monitory poems for a prince (SK 7810, 10988) ; *Versus de alphabeto* (SK 12594) ; *Disticha Catonis* ; Pseudo-Columbanus, *Praecepta vivendi* ; Beda, *De die iudicii* ; 19 anon. Riddles ; Hisperic poems : *Rubisca* (SK 11608) ; *Adelphus* (SK 251) ; Greek alphabet and prayers ; Medical verses (SK 3618, 11969) and excerpts, mainly from Pseudo-Soranus and 'Petrocellus' ; '*Bibliotheca magnifica de sapientia*' (SK 9505) ; The 'Cambridge Songs' (with fifty Latin poems – including five extracts from Statius, Vergil, and Horace – and two

in Latin and Old High German), also possibly including the following 27 extracts from the Metres of Boethius, *De consolatione Philosophiae*, and seven Latin religious poems ; Poem by Pseudo-Vergil (SK 16845) : s. xi med., Canterbury StA?, (prov. ibid.).
FC : A. G. Rigg and G. R. Wieland, *ASE* 4 (1975), 120-129 ; J. M. Ziolkowski, ed., *The Cambridge Songs* (New York, 1994).

13   Hh.1.10   Ælfric, *Grammar*⁺* and *Glossary*⁺* : s. xi³ᐟ⁴, Exeter.

13.5   Ii.2.1   Priscian, *Institutiones grammaticae* (bks. i-xviii, incomplete) with gloss ; Priscian (?), *De accentibus* (f) : s. xi/xii or xii in., Canterbury CC.

14   Ii.2.4   Gregory (Alfred), *Regula pastoralis** : s. xi³ᐟ⁴, Exeter.

15   Ii.2.11   [with Exeter, Cathedral Library, 3501, fols. 0-7]
Records⁺* (s. xi/xii and later) ; Inventory of Leofric's donations to Exeter* ; Donation inscription⁺* ; Gospels with pericope rubrics* ; Gospel of Nicodemus* ; *Vindicta Salvatoris** : s. xi³ᐟ⁴, Exeter.

16   Ii.2.19,   Paulus Diaconus, *Homiliarium* (Easter vigil to fourth Sunday after
          fols. 1-216   Epiphany) [Companion vol. to no. **24**] : s. xi/xii, (prov. Norwich).
FC : Richards (1988), pp. 104-108 ; *Cat. CUL*, III.388-93.

17   Ii.3.33,   'De nativitate S. Mariae' ; Gregory (?), Symbolum fidei ; Gregory,
          fols. 1-194   *Registrum epistolarum* (enlarged version) ; *Conversio Berengarii* (in Gregory VII, *Registrum* VI.17a) : s. xi/xii, Canterbury CC.

18   Ii.4.6   36 Homilies* (most by Ælfric) : s. xi med., Winchester NM, (prov. Tavistock).

19   Ii.6.32   Gospels (only parts of Matthew, Mark, Luke ; John complete) : s. ix or more prob. s. x, prob. Scotland (or Ireland?), (prov. Deer, Cistercian abbey, Aberdeenshire).

20   Kk.1.23,   Ambrose, *Hexameron* : s. xi/xii, Canterbury CC.
          fols. 1-66

20.1   Kk.1.23,   Ambrose, *De paenitentia* ; Augustine (?), *De utilitate agendae*
            fols. 67-135   *paenitentiae (Sermo* 351) ; Augustine, *De utilitate credendi*, *De fide ac symbolo* ; Pseudo-Augustine, *Ad inquisitiones Januarii* (*Epist.* 54, 55) ; Augustine, *Epistola* 127 ; Pseudo-Augustine, *Sermo* 180 ; Augustine, *De excidio urbis Romae* ; Augustine (?), *Sermo* 389, '*Sermo de fide*' ; Augustine, *Sermones* 350, 346-8, 259 : s. xi ex., Canterbury CC.

21	Kk.1.24	[with London, B.L. Cotton Tiberius B.v, fols. 74 and 76, and Sloane 1044, fol. 2] Gospels (Luke, John) ; Records* (s. x^2, x/xi) : s. viii, prob. Northumbria, prov. Ely s. x.
22	Kk.3.18	[?with London, B.L. Cotton Domitian ix, fol. 10] Beda, *Historia ecclesiastica** : s. xi^2, Worcester.
23	Kk.3.21	Boethius, *De consolatione Philosophiae*, with commentary by Remigius (redaction K) ; Poem on the Assumption of the Virgin and dedication poem ; Names of the winds[+]* : s. xi^1 or xi med., prob. Abingdon.
24	Kk.4.13	Paulus Diaconus, *Homiliarium* (Septuagesima to Easter vigil, Sanctorale) [Companion vol. to no. **16**] : s. xi/xii, (prov. Norwich). FC : Richards (1988), pp. 98-101 ; *Cat. CUL*, III.658-663.
25	Kk.5.16	Beda, *Historia ecclesiastica* : c. or after 737, Northumbria, (Wearmouth-J.?), prov. Aachen s. viii ex.
26	Kk.5.32	fols. 49-60 : Calendar ; Computus material ; Excerpts from Byrhtferth's *Enchiridion** (s. xi ex.) : 1012×1030, perh. 1021×1022, Canterbury StA?, prov. SW England s. xi^2 (Glastonbury?). fols. 61-72 and 76 : Dionysius Exiguus, *Cyclus Paschalis*, with added annals and obits : s. xi/xii, W England.
27	Kk.5.34	Augustine, *Quaestiones Evangeliorum* (excerpt, altered) ; Ausonius, *Ephemeris* iii, *Technopaegnion* vi-xiv ; Three Anglo-Latin Poems from Winchester (SK 15226, 5533, 3197) ; Remigius Favius (?), *Carmen de ponderibus et mensuris* (SK 12104) ; Pseudo-Vergil, *Culex*, *Aetna* : s. x ex., prob. Winchester OM or NM, (prov. Glastonbury).
28	Ll.1.10	Prayerbook : Exhortation to prayer* (f) ; Gospel extracts ; Acrostic poem (SK 412) ; 74 Prayers and poems, including *Lorica* of Laidcenn° (SK 15745) and hymn by (Pseudo?-)Hilarius (SK 7445) ; Breviate Psalter ; Harrowing of Hell (liturgical drama?) : c. 820×840, Mercia, prov. Worcester?, (prov. Cerne?).
29	Ll.1.14, fols. 70-108	*Regula S. Benedicti* ; *Memoriale qualiter* ; *Indicium regulae* (on use of hymns) ; *Capitulare monasticum* ; *Ad clericum faciendum* (pontifical ordo) : s. xi^2 or xi ex.
30	Add. 3206	Handbook for a confessor* (f) ; Wulfstan, *Institutes of Polity** (f), '*Canons of Edgar*'* (f) : s. xi^2.
—	Add. 3330	[see no. **857**]

30.5	Add. 4543	Computus material, partly in Welsh (f) : s. x^1 (prob. before 930) or x med. or later, Wales, prov. England s. x? (or in Wales throughout the Middle Ages?).
—	Add. 6000(40)	[see no. **30.8**]
30.8	Inc.5.B.3.97 [1709], binding slips	Gradual (f) : s. xi/xii, Canterbury CC? [Also recorded as Add. MS 6000(40)].

Cambridge, Clare College

31	17	Smaragdus, *Diadema monachorum* : s. xi ex. or xii in., England or France, (prov. s. $xii^{2/4}$ England).
32	18	Orosius, *Historiae adversus paganos* ; Justinus, Epitome of Pompeius Trogus, *Historiae Philippicae* (part) : s. xi/xii or xii in., prob. St. Albans.
34	30 pt. i	Gregory, *Dialogi* : s. xi^2 or $xi^{3/4}$, Worcester.
34.1	30 pt. ii	Defensor of Ligugé, *Liber Scintillarum* ; Julian of Toledo, *Prognosticon futuri saeculi* ; Alcuin, *De fide sanctae et individuae Trinitatis* (incomplete) : s. xi^2 or $xi^{3/4}$, Worcester.
35	s.n. (pastedown)	Solinus, *Collectanea* (f) : s. xi ex. or xii in., Bury St. Edmunds.
35.5	s.n.	Orosius, *Historiae adversus paganos* (f) : s. xi^2, Bury St. Edmunds.

Cambridge, Corpus Christi College

36	9	pp. 1-60 : Calendar ; Computus material and Easter tables : s. xi^2 ; Four additional Vitae : s. xi ex. and xii in., Worcester. pp. 61-458 [with London, B.L. Cotton Nero E.i, vol. ii, fols. 166-180] : Office legendary (October - December) [Companion vol. to no. **344**] : s. $xi^{3/4}$, Worcester. FC : Jackson and Lapidge (1996).
37	12	Gregory (Alfred), *Regula pastoralis** : s. x^2, Worcester?, (prov. ibid.).
38	23 vol. i	Gennadius, On Prudentius (*De viris illustribus*, ch. xiii) ; Prudentius, *Psychomachia, Peristephanon* ; Epigrams for the basilica of St. Agnes by Constantia (SK 2659) and Damasus (SK 4939) ; Prudentius, *Contra Symmachum* (f) ; (works by Prudentius with glosses ; *Psychomachia* illustrations with OE titles, s. x/xi - xi/xii) : s. x^2 or

x ex. or xi in., S England (Canterbury? SW England?), prov. Malmesbury prob. by s. xi[1].

39	41	Beda, *Historia ecclesiastica** ; Mass sets (from a sacramentary) ; Office chants ; Old English Martyrology* (f) ; Charms[(*)]; *Solomon and Saturn** (f) ; Medical recipe* ; Six homilies* ; Apocalypse of Thomas* ; Gospel of Nicodemus* ; Prayers ; Donation inscription[+]* (s. xi[3/4]) : s. xi[1] ; OE texts, except Beda, and liturgical texts are additions of s. xi[1] - xi med. ; prob. S England, prov. Exeter by s. xi[3/4].
40	44	Excerpt from Amalarius, *Liber officialis* III.i* ; Pontifical : s. xi[2/4] or xi med. or xi[3/4], Canterbury (StA or CC?), (prov. Ely).
41	57	*Regula S. Benedicti* with interpolations (and glosses s. xi) ; Ambrosius Autpertus (Pseudo-Fulgentius), Admonition ; *Memoriale qualiter* ; '*De festivitatibus anni*' (*Ansegisi capitularium collectio*, ii.33) ; *Capitulare monasticum* ; Martyrologium (Usuard ; with additions and necrology s. xi med. and later) ; Two formula-letters announcing the death of a monastic priest or deacon ; Smaragdus, *Diadema monachorum* (incomplete) : s. x/xi, Abingdon or Canterbury?, prov. Abingdon.
42	69	Gregory, *Homiliae in Evangelia*, bk.ii (*Hom.* 21-40) : s. viii ex./ix in. or ix[1], S England.
—	111, pp. 7, 8, 55 and 56	[see no. **44**]
43	130	Decreta Pontificum and Concilia (Lanfranc's Collection) ; Lanfranc, *Epistola* 49 ; Lists of popes (add. s. xii[1]) and Roman emperors : s. xi/xii or xii in., SW England.
44	140	[with 111, pp. 7, 8, 55 and 56] Gospels* : s. xi[1] ; Manumissions* ; Homily* ; Lists of popes and English bishops (s. xi/xii) ; List of relics* ; Agreement of confraternity* : s. xi[2] ; origin all parts Bath.
45	144	Two glossaries[+]* : s. ix[1], S England, prob. SW England, (prov. Canterbury StA).
46	146	Pontifical, Benedictional : s. xi in., Winchester OM (or Canterbury CC??) ; Supplement (pp. 1-60, 319-330) : Worcester, s. xi[2] - xii in.
48	153	Martianus Capella, *De nuptiis Philologiae et Mercurii* with Welsh glosses : s. ix ex. or x[1/3], Wales, supplemented in England s. x[1] ; Latin distich (SK 15273) ; Dunchad (Martin of Laon?), Commentary on Martianus Capella : s. x[1] or x med. or x[3/4], S England, perh. Canterbury.

50	162, pp. 1-138, 161-564	Homilies* (most by Ælfric) : s. x ex. or xi in., SE England.
—	162, pp. 139-160	[see no. **54**]

51   163   Pontifical (Pontificale Romano-Germanicum) ; Blessings ;
Benediction ; Hymn (SK 5629) ; Sermon ; parts of Office of the
Dead : s. xi^2, prob. xi$^{4/4}$, prob. Worcester (Winchester OM? at or
for Nunnaminster?).
FC : M. Lapidge, *TCBS*, VIII, pt. 1 (1981), 24-26 and 20-21.

52   173, fols.   West-Saxon royal genealogy* : s. ix/x ; *Anglo-Saxon Chronicle* A* :
         1-56   s. ix/x - xi^2 ; Acta Lanfranci : s. xi ex. ; Laws* : *Alfred* and *Ine* :
s. x$^{2/4}$; Lists of popes and English bishops : s. x^2 or x ex. - xii in. ;
Wessex, perh. Winchester, prov. Winchester by s. x med., prov.
Canterbury CC s. xi ex. or xii in.

53   173, fols.   Sedulius, Letters I and II to Macedonius (s. ix), *Carmen Paschale*°,
         57-83   two Hymns° ; Verses by Damasus on St. Paul (SK 7486) ; Excerpts
from Augustine, *De civitate Dei*, xviii.23, with three versions of
Sibylline prophecies : s. viii^2, S England, prob. Kent, prov. Winchester
from s. ix ex. or x in.?, prov. Canterbury CC.

54   178, pp.   [with 162, pp. 139-160]
         1-270   Ælfric, *Hexameron**, (version of Alcuin's) *Interrogationes Sigewulfi
in Genesin**, Homilies*, *De duodecim abusivis saeculi** ; Two anon.
texts* : s. xi^1, prov. Worcester.

55   178, pp.   *Regula S. Benedicti*$^+$* ; On the Seven Ages of the World* : s. xi^1,
         287-457   prob. Worcester, (prov. ibid.).

56   183   Beda, *Vita S. Cuthberti* (prose) ; Lists of popes, of the seventy
disciples of Christ, of English bishops and kings ; Notes : on the
Incarnation of Christ, the Ages of the World, the Ages of Man, the
human body, on the dimensions of the world, the Temple of Solomon
at Jerusalem, the Jewish Tabernacle, St. Peter's in Rome, Noah's Ark,
on the books of the Bible and the number of Psalms, on measures of
length, on the Creation ; Glossary$^{(+*)}$; Beda, *Vita S. Cuthberti*
(verse) ; Mass and Office of St. Cuthbert, with Hymn and Sequence
(SK 9224, 7173) ; List of vessels* (s. x) ; Record* (s. xi^2) : 934×939,
S England, (Wessex? Winchester? Glastonbury?), prov. Chester-le-
Street, prov. Durham.

57   187   Eusebius (Rufinus), *Historia ecclesiastica* : s. xi/xii, prob. Canterbury
CC, (prov. ibid.).

58   188   Ælfric, *Hexameron** (incomplete), *Catholic Homilies* (First Series,
expanded)* : s. xi^1, perh. xi$^{2/4}$, (prov. Hereford Cathedral?).

59	190, pp. iii-xii, 1-294	(A version of Wulfstan's 'Handbook') : *Poenitentiale Pseudo-Theodori* ; Wulfstan's Canon Law Collection (*'Excerptiones Pseudo-Egberti'*, recension B, partial text) ; Texts and excerpts concerned with ecclesiastical law and the liturgy ; Ælfric, Pastoral Letters 2 and 3 ; Wulfstan, Homily VIIIa ; Benedictions ; Alcuin, *Epistolae* 16f, 17, 114 ; *De ecclesiasticis gradibus* ; Hrabanus Maurus, *De institutione clericorum* II.1-10 ; Ordo Romanus XIIIA ; *De ecclesiastica consuetudine* (including excerpts from *Regularis Concordia* and Amalarius, *Liber officialis*) ; *'Institutio beati Amalarii'* (excerpts from *Liber officialis*) ; Abbo of Saint-Germain, Three abbrev. sermons ; Excerpts from Defensor of Ligugé, *Liber scintillarum* ; Adso, *De Antichristo* : s. xi^1, Worcester?, prov. Exeter by xi med. Exeter additions s. xi med. - xi^2 : Hymn (SK 11017) ; Excerpts from Decreta and Councils, and from *Collectio canonum Hibernensis* ; Charm* ; Capitula of canons of Councils of Winchester (1070) and Windsor (1070) ; Penitential articles issued after the Battle of Hastings. FC : Budny (1997), i.541-542 ; cf. Sauer (2000), p. 378.

59.5	190, pp. 295-420	pp. 319-350 and 365-420 : Ælfric, Pastoral Letters II* and III* ; Ordines for Easter vigil and Whitsun vigil* ; Penitential (*'Confessionale Pseudo-Egberti'*)* ; Excerpt from Chrodegang, *Regula canonicorum* (enlarged version, ch. 83)* ; Penitential (*'Poenitentiale Pseudo-Egberti'*)* ; Excerpts concerned with confession and penitence* ; Laws* : *Mirce, Að, Hadbot* : s. xi med. pp. 295-318 and 351-364 : Ælfric, Pastoral Letter I* ; *De ecclesiasticis gradibus* ; Three homilies* (one by Ælfric) : s. xi$^{3/4}$, Exeter, whole MS prov. Exeter.

60	191	Chrodegang, *Regula canonicorum* (enlarged version)$^+$* : s. xi$^{3/4}$, Exeter.

61	192	Amalarius, *Liber officialis* (Retractatio prima) ; Excerpts from Eusebius (Rufinus), *Historia ecclesiastica*, and works of Jerome ; Ordo Romanus XXXII (added) : s. x med. (prob. 952), Landévennec, prov. England (Canterbury StA?) s. x^2, (prov. prob. Canterbury CC). FC : Budny (1997), i.202.

61.5	193	Ambrose, *Hexameron* : s. ix$^{2-3/3}$, prob. N France, perh. Soissons, prov. England by s. xi?

62	196	Old English Martyrology* ; *Vindicta Salvatoris** : s. xi^2, Exeter.

63	197B	[with London, B.L. Cotton Otho C.v and Royal 7.C.xii, fols. 2 and 3] Gospels (f) : s. vii/viii or viii in., Northumbria (prob. Lindisfarne), prov. S England (Canterbury StA?) s. viii^2/ix in.

64	198	Homilies* (most by Ælfric) ; A version of the Phoenix story* ; Office of St. Guthlac (part ; s. xi ex.) : s. xi^1, Worcester? additions s. xi^2 W England, (prov. Worcester).
65	201, pp. 1-7, 161-167	*Regularis Concordia**(f) ; Beda, *De die iudicii** ('*Judgement Day II*') ; Exhortation to Christian living*, Summons to prayer* : s. xi in.
65.5	201, pp. 8-160, 167-176	On the Seven Ages of the World$^+$* ; Homilies$^{(*)}$ (twenty by Wulfstan) ; Ælfric, Pastoral Letter II (revised version)* ; A collection of Anglo-Saxon Laws* ; Wulfstan, *Institutes of Polity*, '*Canons of Edgar*'* ; *De ecclesiasticis gradibus** ; 'Benedictine Office'* (with excerpts from Hrabanus Maurus, *De clericorum institutione* II.1-10) ; Handbook for a confessor* ; *Apollonius of Tyrus** ; Resting-places of English saints* ; Genesis* (part, from OE Hexateuch) ; Lord's Prayer and Gloria in verse* ; Forms of absolution and confession : s. xi^1 or xi med., Winchester NM?
66	201, pp. 179-262	Theodulf of Orléans, *Capitula*$^+$* ; Homily* ; Martyrologium (Usuard ; f ; s. xi ex.) : s. xi$^{3/4}$, Exeter. [orig. joined with no. **60**?]
67	206	Martianus Capella, *De nuptiis Philologiae et Mercurii*, bk.iv ; Alcuin, *carm.* 72 (part) ; Themistius, *De decem categoriis*, with notes ; Pseudo-Apuleius, *Peri hermenias* (incomplete) ; Porphyrius (Boethius), *Isagoge* ; *Glosae de Isagogis* (from second Commentary by Boethius) ; Boethius, Five theological works, with gloss ; Alcuin, *De dialectica* ; Augustine (?), *De dialectica* : s. x^1, England (perh. Canterbury) rather than NE France, prov. England (Canterbury, or St. Albans, or Bury St. Edmunds?) s. xi/xii.
68	214	Boethius, *De consolatione Philosophiae*° : s. x ex. or xi in., Canterbury?
69	221, fols. 1-24	Alcuin, *De orthographia* (incomplete) ; Beda, *De orthographia* : s. x^1 or x med. or x^2, perh. Canterbury StA (or Brittany?).
69.5	221, fols. 25-64	Cassiodorus, *De orthographia* ; Caper, *De orthographia* ; Agroecius, *Ars de orthographia* : s. x, England (? or s. ix Continent, prov. England s. x or xi).
70	223	French regnal list (with additions) ; Four recipes, three medical (s. x) ; Gennadius, On Prudentius (*De viris illustribus*, ch. xiii) ; Prudentius, *Cathemerinon, Apotheosis, Hamartigenia* (Computus note add. s. x/xi England), *Psychomachia, Peristephanon, Contra Symmachum, Dittochaeon, Epilogus* ; Johannes Scottus, *carm.* 9 (SK 1417) ; s. ix$^{3/4}$, Arras, Saint-Vaast, prov. s. ix ex. Saint-Bertin, prov. England s. x^1.

Additions in England : Pontifical prayer ; Benedictions ; Gregory, *Registrum epistolarum* XI.4 (f) ; Two alphabets : s. x/xi ; Latin and OE glosses : s. x and xi.

72	260	Boethius, *De institutione musica*, V.xvi-xix ; *Musica Enchiriadis* ; *Scolica Enchiriadis* ; *Commemoratio brevis de tonis* : s. x^2 or x ex., Canterbury CC.
73	265, pp. 1-268	pp. 1-268 : (A version of Wulfstan's 'Handbook') : Alcuin, *Epistolae* 17, 114 ; First Capitulary of Gerbald of Liège ; *Poenitentiale Egberti* (Prologue and chs. i-xiii) ; Wulfstan's Canon Law Collection ('*Excerptiones Pseudo-Egberti*', recension A) ; Excerpts mainly from *Poenitentiale Pseudo-Theodori* and other penitentials, and from Theodulfi *Capitula* ; Handbook for a confessor* ; Excerpts from : *Ansegisi capitularium collectio* and other capitularies, from *Admonitio generalis* and *Institutio canonicorum* of Aachen Council of 816, from collection of canons ; Abbo of Saint-Germain, Sermo II ; Ælfric, Pastoral Letters 2 and 3 ; Wulfstan, Homily VIIIa ; *De officio missae* ; *De ecclesiaticis gradibus* ; Hrabanus Maurus, *De institutione clericorum* II.1-7 ; Forms of excommunication ; Laws : *Eadgar IV'* * ; Chrism mass ordo ; Ælfric, Letter to the monks of Eynsham : s. xi med. - $xi^{3/4}$, Worcester.

pp. 269-367 : Excerpts from Amalarius, *Liber officialis* (complete version) ; Excerpts from Pontificale Romano-Germanicum ; Amalarius (?), *Eclogae de ordine Romano* : s. xi^2, Worcester.
pp. 368-442 ; Bernold of Constance, *Micrologus de ecclesiasticis observationibus* ; *De ordine missae, De antiphonis* : s. xi ex. or xii in., Worcester.
FC : Budny (1997), i. 605-607. See also Sauer (2000), p. 377, and Cross and Hamer (1999), pp. 41-48.

74	267	Verses from service for St. Mellitus ; Freculf of Lisieux, *Chronicon*, pt. i : s. xi/xii, Canterbury StA.
75	270, fols. 1 and 197	Beda, *Historia ecclesiastica* (f) : s. xi ex. or xi/xii, prob. Canterbury StA.
76	270, fols. 2-173	Sacramentary : 1091×1100, Canterbury StA. FC : *The Missal of Saint Augustine's Abbey Canterbury*, ed. M. Rule (Cambridge, 1896).
77	272	Psalterium Gallicanum with psalter collects (and with commentary mainly from Cassiodorus : England s. xi med. or xi^2) ; Litany ; Canticles ; Prayers and responsories : 883×884, Rheims, prov. England s. xi, (prov. Canterbury CC).

79	276, fols. 1-54	Eutropius, *Breviarium*, with additions and continuation by Paulus Diaconus ('*Historia Romana*') ; spurious charter by Pope Leo VIII : s. xi ex., Canterbury StA.
80	276, fols. 55-134	Dudo of Saint-Quentin, *Historia Normannorum* : s. xi/xii, Canterbury StA.
81	279	*Sinodus episcoporum* ('First Synod of St. Patrick') ; Collection of canons (Excerpts from the Fathers) ; *Liber ex lege Moysi* with Latin, Irish and Breton glosses ; Excerpts from *Collectio canonum Hibernensis* (recension A) : s. ix/x or x in., NW France, perh. in or near Tours, prov. England by c. 1000, (prov. Worcester).
82	285, fols. 75-131	Aldhelm, *De virginitate* (verse) : s. xi in.
83	286	Gospels ; Documents* (s. x) : s. vi^2 or vi/vii, Italy (Rome?), prov. S England (Minster-in-Thanet?) s. vii/viii, perh. Canterbury s. viii/ix, prov. Canterbury StA s. x (or ix?).
85	291	Beda, *De temporum ratione* ; Isidore, *De positione vii stellarum errantium* (= *De natura rerum*, 23) ; Beda, *Epistola ad Wicthedum* ; Computus material and Paschal tables : s. xi/xii, Canterbury StA.
86	302	Ælfric, *Hexameron** ; Homilies* (most by Ælfric) : s. xi/xii.
87	304	Isidore (?), *Versus in bibliotheca* (SK 15860 ; excerpts) ; Juvencus, *Libri Evangeliorum* : s. viii^1, Italy, prov. s. ix ex. or x in. England (Canterbury CC? Malmesbury?).
88	307 pt. 1, fols. 1-52	Felix, *Vita S. Guthlaci* ; Two acrostic poems (SK 4297, 2361 ; s. x med.) : s. x in., Worcester?
88.5	309, flyleaves	Sallust, *Bellum Jugurthinum* (f) : s. xi ex. or xi/xii, England or more prob. Continent. In England by 1100?
90	320, fols. 117-170	Two exhortations* (s. x/xi) ; *Poenitentiale Theodori* (incomplete); Gregory and Augustine, *Libellus responsionum* ; Poem by Archbishop Theodore (SK 16100) ; Order of confession ; *Poenitentiale Sangermanense* ; Chronological and other notes, as in no. **56** : s. x^2 or x ex., Canterbury StA.
91	321, fol. 139*	Dialogue on Alleluia* : s. xi^1 or xi med.
92	322	Gregory (Werferth), *Dialogi** : s. xi^2, Worcester?, (prov. Worcester?).
93	326	'Aldhelm'* (poem) ; Aldhelm, *De virginitate* (prose)° ; Abbo of Saint-Germain, *Bella Parisiacae urbis* iii.1-17 ; Glosses ; Sententiae ; On Adam's creation ; Latin poem (SK 10046) ;

De ebrietate (extract from Florilegium) ; Three Latin notes, one on grammar ; Rota poem (SK 11297) : s. x/xi, Canterbury CC.

94	328, pp. 1-80	Osbern, *Vita S. Dunstani* ; Mass of St. Dunstan, and sequence : s. xi/xii or xii in., Canterbury CC?, (prov. Winchester OM).
95	330 pt. i	Martianus Capella, *De nuptiis Philologiae et Mercurii* ; List of the Muses ; Verses on the Muses (SK 2425) : s. xi/xii or xii in., Normandy? Malmesbury?, (prov. Malmesbury).
96	330 pt. ii	Dunchad (Martin of Laon?), Commentary on Martianus Capella ; Glossae collectae : s. ix ex., France, prov. England s. x, (prov. Malmesbury).
97	352	Boethius, *De institutione arithmetica* (with scholia s. x and xi/xii) : s. x med. or x^2, prob. Canterbury StA, (prov. ibid.).
98	356 pt. iii	Glossary ; Hebrew alphabet ; Medical recipe (s. xi) : s. x^2 or $x^{4/4}$, prob. Canterbury StA.
99	361	Gregory, *Regula pastoralis* ; *Passio S. Mauricii* (f ; s. xi/xii ; *BHL* 5747d?) : s. xi med. or xi^2, England? Malmesbury?, (prov. Malmesbury).
100	367 pt. ii, fols. 45-52	Goscelin (?), *Vita brevior* of St. Kenelm (lections ii part, iii-viii) ; Booklist* ; Vision of Leofric* (s. xi^2) ; Sequence (SK 8630 ; s. xi^2) : s. xi med., prob. Worcester.
101	368	*Regula S. Benedicti* (incomplete) : s. x/xi.
102	383	A collection of Anglo-Saxon laws* ; Charm* ; Record* ; West-Saxon royal genealogy* (incomplete) : s. xi/xii, prob. London, St. Paul's.
103	389	Jerome, *Vita S. Pauli Eremitae* ; Felix, *Vita S. Guthlaci* : s. x^2 or $x^{3/4}$ or x ex., Canterbury StA ; Frontispiece added ibid. s. xi med.
104	391	Computus material ; Calendar ; Psalterium Gallicanum ; Hymnal ; Canticles ; Monastic canticles ; Collectar with Office chants ; Exorcisms, Blessings, Ordeals ; Prayers[+]* ; Offices ; Votive offices ; Prognostics* : s. $xi^{3/4}$, Worcester. FC : *The Portiforium of Saint Wulstan*, ed. A. Hughes, HBS 89, 90 (1958-60) [Collectar and following texts only] ; Gneuss (1968) ; Korhammer (1976).
105	399	Julian of Toledo, *Prognosticon futuri saeculi* : s. ix^1 or ix med., N France (W France?), prov. England by s. x^1.

106	411	Mass chants (s. xi/xii or xii) ; Psalterium Gallicanum, with scholia ; Canticles ; Two litanies (one added s. x/xi) ; Prayers ; Seven gospel pericopes (add. s. xii) : s. x^2, Canterbury (CC?), or s. x^1, W France (Loire valley : Tours?)?, prov. Abingdon?, (prov. Canterbury).
107	415	Norman Anonymous, Tracts : s. xi/xii or xii in., Normandy or England?
108	419	[with 421, pp. 1 and 2] Fifteen Homilies* (six by Wulfstan) ; Prayer* [Companion vol. to no. **109**] : s. xi^1, prob. SE England (Canterbury?), prov. Exeter.
109	421	Fifteen Homilies* (ten by Ælfric) : fols. 99-208, 225-354 [Companion vol. to no. **108**] : s. xi^1, prob. Canterbury ; fols. 3-98, 209-224 : s. xi$^{3/4}$, Exeter, prov. all parts Exeter.
110	422, pp. 1-26	*Solomon and Saturn** (verse and prose) : s. x^1 or x$^{2/4}$ or x med.
111	422, pp. 27-570	Lunarium$^+$* ; Calendar ; Computus material$^{(*)}$; Prognostics* ; Masses ; Manual services ; Offices : s. xi med. (1060/61?), prob. Winchester (NM?), prov. Sherborne?, (prov. prob. Darley Dale, Derbyshire, church of St. Helen).
112	430	Martinus of Braga, *Formula honestae vitae* ; Ferrandus Diaconus, *Ad Reginum comitem* ; Ambrosius Autpertus, *Sermo de cupiditate* : s. ix ex. or ix/x, Saint-Amand, prov. s. x England (prob. Canterbury StA), (prov. Glastonbury).
114	448	fols. 1-86 : Prosper, *Epigrammata, Versus ad coniugem* ; Isidore, *Synonyma* : s. x^1 or x med., S England (or Worcester?). fols. 87-103 : Sybilline prophecies (SK 8495) ; *Physiologus* (lion, unicorn, panther only) ; Latin poems (including SK 10279 by Pseudo-Vergil) ; Note on the languages of the world ; Prosper, *Sententiae ex operibus S. Augustini*, no. 390 ; Prudentius, *Peristephanon* (Prologue only), *Dittochaeon* ; *Septem miracula mundi* : s. xi/xii, S England (or Worcester?), (prov. whole MS Winchester).
115	449, fols. 42-96	Ælfric, *Grammar*$^+$* (incomplete ; fols. 1-41 supplied s. xvi) and *Glossary*$^+$* : s. xi^1.
116	473	Troper (Cantatorium) : s. x/xi or xi$^{2/4}$, with additions s. xi^1 and later, Winchester OM. FC : Budny (1997), i. 490-491 ; Frere (1894) ; Planchart (1977).
117	557	[with Lawrence, University of Kansas, Kenneth Spencer Research Library, Pryce C2 :1] Homily (for *Inventio s. Crucis*)* (f) : s. xi med., Worcester?, (prov. Worcester).

—   EP-0-6 (ptd. bk.)   [see no. **648**]

Cambridge, Fitzwilliam Museum

118   88-1972,   Gospel lectionary with collects, and some homilies on Temporale
          fols. 2-43   gospels : s. xi/xii or xii in., Canterbury?, (prov. Shrewsbury).

118.5 88-1972,   Gospel lectionary with collects (incomplete) : s. xi/xii or xii in.,
          fols. 44-56   prob. Canterbury StA, (prov. Shrewsbury).

119   45-1980   Gospels (incomplete), Gospel list : s. ix ex., W France (Brittany,
                                Dol region?), or Loire valley?, prov. England by s. x med.

Cambridge, Gonville and Caius College

120   144/194   Remigius, Commentaries on Sedulius (*Carmen paschale* and Hymns)
                                and on *Disticha Catonis* (part) ; Sermon (f) ; verse excerpts from :
                                Prudentius (*Hamartigenia*), Dungal, *Monosticha Catonis*, Venantius
                                Fortunatus (SK 10856, 13757, 16396 lines 1-32, 1112, 5349 ; 4382
                                anon.) ; Pseudo-Columbanus, *Praecepta vivendi* ; Prudentius,
                                Dittochaeon, XLV-XLIX, XL-XLII : s. x^1, England?, prov.
                                Canterbury StA.

120.3 466/573, two   Missal (f) : s. xi med.
          endleaves

120.6 734/782a   Mass lectionary (f) : s. xi^1, Canterbury CC.

121   820 (h)   Bible (f ; from Minor prophets) : s. viii ex.

Cambridge, Jesus College

121.5 5 (Q.A.5)   Missal (f) : s. xi^1.
          flyleaves

122   15 (Q.A.15),   Ælfric, Homilies* (f) : s. xi^1, (prov. Durham).
          fols. i-x and 1-10
          (binding leaves)

123   28 (Q.B.11)   Greek alphabet ; Priscian, *Institutiones grammaticae* (bks. i-xvi),
                                Priscian (?) *De accentibus* (incomplete) : s. xi ex., France, (prov.
                                Durham).

Cambridge, Magdalene College

124   Pepys 2981 (2)   [with London, B.L. Sloane 1086, fol. 119]
Gospels (f) : s. viii^2.

125   Pepys 2981 (3)   Psalterium Romanum (f) : s. ix/x.

126   Pepys 2981 (4)   Bible (f ; from Daniel) : s. ix^1, prob. Northumbria.

127   Pepys 2981 (5)   Remigius, Scholia on Martianus Capella (f) : s. ix/x or x^1, Winchester.

127.3   Pepys 2981 (7)   Priscian, *Institutiones grammaticae* (f) : s. xi^2, England?

—   Pepys 2981 (16)   [see no. **442**]

—   Pepys 2981 (18)   [see no. **219**]

—   Pepys 2981 (19)   [see no. **220**]

127.6   Pepys 2981 (52)   Missal (f) : s. xi, France, or England?

Cambridge, Pembroke College

128   17   Jerome, *In Isaiam*, bks. viii-xviii : s. ix^1 or ix med., Tours area, prov. England s. xi, (prov. Bury St. Edmunds).

129   23   Paulus Diaconus, *Homiliarium* (Easter to Advent) [Companion vol. to no. **130**] : s. xi^2, France (Saint-Denis?), prov. by s. xi/xii England, (prov. Bury St. Edmunds).
FC : James (1905), pp. 20-22.

130   24   Paulus Diaconus, *Homiliarium* (Sanctorale, Commune SS.) [Companion vol. to no. **129**] : s. xi^2, France (Saint-Denis?), prov. by s. xi/xii England, (prov. Bury St. Edmunds).
FC : James (1905), pp. 23-25.

131   25   Homiliarium of Saint-Père, Chartres ; Hrabanus Maurus, *De institutione clericorum*, II.1-10 ; Sequence (SK 575) : s. xi ex. or xi^2, (prov. Bury St. Edmunds).
FC : J. E. Cross, *Cambridge Pembroke College 25* (London, 1987).

132   41   Augustine, *Enchiridion* : s. xi in. or xi$^{1/4}$, Canterbury CC?, (prov. Bury St. Edmunds).

132.3   46, fols. A and B   Gradual (f) : s. x$^{2/4}$ or x med., (prov. Bury St. Edmunds).

132.4	46, fols. 82 and 83	Sacramentary (f) : s. x, France (Brittany?), (prov. Bury St. Edmunds).
133	81	Beda, *De templo Salomonis*, *In Regum libros*, *In Canticum Habacuc* : s. ix$^{2/3}$, S France?, (prov. Bury St. Edmunds).
134	83	Record* (s. xi/xii) ; Beda, *In Evangelium Lucae* : s. ix^1 or ix med., Saint-Denis, prov. Bury St. Edmunds s. xi^2.
135	88	Record* (s. xi) ; Laidcenn, *Egloga de Moralibus in Job* : s. x^1, France (Saint-Denis?) (or England?), prov. Canterbury StA by s. x^2, (prov. Bury St. Edmunds).
136	91	Jerome, *Tractatus in Psalmos* ; Verse epilogue (SK 9575) ; Macedonian names of the months ; Anon. Letter ; *Translatio S. Bartholomaei* (f) : s. ix$^{1/3}$, N France, (prov. Bury St. Edmunds).
136.5	103*	Service-book (f) : s. xi.
137	108	*Edictum Justiniani de fide* (*Confessio fidei*) ; Pseudo-Jerome, *Libellus fidei ad Damasum* (*Epistola supp.* 16) ; Augustine, *Oratio de Trinitate* ; Prosper (??), *De fide, de spe et de caritate* ; Vigilius Thapsensis, *Contra Arianos, Sabellianos, Photinianos*, (?) *Dialogus contra Arianos* ; Eusebius (Rufinus), *Historia ecclesiastica* (excerpt) : s. ix$^{2/3}$, E France, (prov. Bury St. Edmunds).
138	301	Gospels : s. xi in. or xi^1, Peterborough?
139	302	Gospel lectionary ; Hereford diocesan boundaries* (add. s. xi^2) : s. xi med., Canterbury?, prov. Hereford Cathedral.
140	308	Hrabanus Maurus, *In Epistolas Pauli*, bks. ix-xix : s. ix^2, Rheims, prov. England s. ix ex.?, (prov. Ely).
141	312C, nos. 1 and 2	[with Haarlem, Stadsbibliotheek, 188 F 53, and Sondershausen, Schlossbibliothek Br 1] Psalterium Gallicanum° (f) : s. xi med., prov. Flanders by 1069, Bruges from 1087?
142	312C, no. 5	Venantius Fortunatus, *Carmina* (f) : s. x/xi.
143	313/20	Pontifical (f) : s. xi^2 or xi/xii, Bury St. Edmunds?
143.5	C.8 (ptd. bk.), pastedowns	Missal (f) : s. xi.

Cambridge, Peterhouse

144   74

Decreta Pontificum and Concilia (Lanfranc's Collection) ; Papal letters : 1081×1088, and later additions, prov. Durham s. xi ex.

145   251, fols. 106-191

Galen, *Ad Glauconem de medendi methodo,* and *Liber tertius* ; *Liber Aurelii de acutis passionibus* ; *Liber Esculapii de chronicis passionibus* ; Galen (attrib.), *De podagra* : s. xi ex. or xi/xii, Canterbury StA.

Cambridge, Queens' College

146   (Horne) 75

[with Oxford, Bodleian Library, Eng.th.c.74 ; Bloomington, Indiana University, Lilly Library, Poole 40, and New Haven, Yale University, Beinecke Library, Osborn fa 26]
Ælfric, Homilies* (f) and Lives of Saints* (f) : s. xi in.

Cambridge, St. John's College

147   35 (B.13)

Gregory, *Homiliae in Ezechielem* : s. xi ex., (prov. Bury St. Edmunds).

148   59 (C.9)

Psalterium Gallicanum with glosses (Latin and Irish) ; Prayers ; Canticles : s. x/xi, Ireland, (prov. Dover), in England before 1100?

149   73 (C.23)

Gospels, Gospel list : s. xi/xii, Bury St. Edmunds.

150   82 (D.7), fols. 89-92

Canticles (f) : s. x med. [presumably from a psalter MS].

151   87 (D.12), fols. 1-50

Statius, *Thebais* : s. xi^2, France, (prov. Dover), in England before 1100?

152   101 (D.26), fols. 1-14

Cassian, *De institutis monachorum,* bk.xii : s. x^2, Canterbury StA (Glastonbury?).

153   164 (F.27)

Adrevald of Fleury, *Historia translationis S. Benedicti* ; parts of rhymed offices for St. Augustine of Canterbury and Abbot Hadrian (s. xi) ; Adrevald, *Miracula S. Benedicti* ; Sermon : s. x, prob. England, (prov. Canterbury StA).

153.5   236 (L.9)

Acts of the Council of London 1074×1075 : c. 1075, Canterbury CC.

154   Aa.5.1, fol. 67

Cassiodorus, *In Psalmos* (f) : s. viii^1, Northumbria, or s. viii or ix^1, S England?, (prov. Ramsey).

154.5   Ii.12.29 (ptd.   Isidore, *Etymologiae* (f) : s. ix^1 or ix med., France.
          bk.), flyleaves

Cambridge, Sidney Sussex College

155   Δ.5.15 (100)   Pontifical services : s. x$^{3/3}$, prob. Winchester OM (Ramsey??) ; Mass
          pt. ii   of St. Cuthbert ; Antiphons for the Office of St. Nicholas (s. xi/xii) :
                           s. xi^1, Durham (or Wessex), prov. whole MS Durham.
                           FC : Banting (1989), pp. 157-170.

Cambridge, Trinity College

155.5   B.1.16 (15)   Berengaudus, *In Apocalypsin* ; Haimo of Auxerre, *In Canticum*
                           canticorum (incomplete) : s. xi/xii, Canterbury CC, (prov. ibid?).

156   B.1.29 (27),   Pseudo-Jerome, *In Canticum canticorum* : s. xi/xii, France,
          fols. 1-47   (prov. Buildwas, Cistercian abbey), in England before 1100?

157   B.1.30A (28) [with New Haven, Yale University, Beinecke Library, 320]
                           Pontifical (f) : s. x$^{2/4}$ or x med.

158   B.1.40 (38)   Augustine, *De diversis quaestionibus LXXXIII* : s. xi ex.,
                           Canterbury StA.

159   B.1.42 (40)   Cyprianus Gallus, *Pentateuchos* : s. x^2, Canterbury StA.

161   B.3.5 (84)   Jerome, *In Prophetas minores, In Danielem* : s. xi ex.,
                           Canterbury CC.

162   B.3.9 (88)   Ambrose, *In Evangelium Lucae* : s. xi/xii, Canterbury CC.

162.6 B.3.14 (93)   Richard of Préaux, *In Genesin*, pt. ii [Companion vol. to no. **504.8**] :
                           s. xi/xii, Préaux, (prov. Canterbury CC).

163   B.3.25 (104) Augustine, *Confessiones* with *Retractationes* II.vi, *De haeresibus* :
                           s. xi ex. (1080s), Canterbury CC.

164   B.3.33 (112) Augustine, *De adulterinis coniugiis, De mendacio, Contra*
                           mendacium, De cura pro mortuis gerenda, De vera religione,
                           De natura et origine animae ; Pseudo-Augustine, *Sermo Arianorum,*
                           Contra sermonem Arianorum (from Syagrius, *Regulae definitionum*) ;
                           Augustine, *Contra adversarium legis et prophetarum* : s. xi/xii,
                           Canterbury CC.

165   B.4.2 (116)   Gospel of St. John ; Augustine, *In Evangelium Johannis :* s. xi ex.,
                           Canterbury CC.

165.5	B.4.5 (119)	Florus of Lyon, *In Epistolas Pauli ad Romanos, ad Corinthios I* [Companion vol. to no. **567.5**] : s. xi/xii, Préaux, (prov. Canterbury CC).
166	B.4.9 (123)	Gregory, *Moralia*, bks. 17-35 : s. xi/xii, Canterbury CC.
167	B.4.26 (140)	Augustine, *Epistolae* : s. xi ex., Canterbury CC.
168	B.4.27 (141)	Isidore, *Quaestiones in Vetus Testamentum* ; Adalbert of Metz, *Speculum Gregorii* (epitome of *Moralia*) ; Augustine, *In Epistolam Johannis ad Parthos* : s. x ex., Canterbury CC.
—	B.5.2 (148)	[see no. **270**]
169.5	B.5.24 (170)	Jerome, *In Isaiam*, bks. 11-18 ; s. xi/xii, Canterbury CC.
170	B.5.26 (172)	Augustine, *In Psalmos* (1-50) [Companion volumes : nos. **171** and **937.5**] : s. xi ex., Canterbury CC.
171	B.5.28 (174)	Augustine, *In Psalmos* (101-150) : s. xi ex., Canterbury CC [cf. no. **170**].
172	B.10.4 (215)	Gospels, Gospel list : s. xi$^{1/4}$, Canterbury CC? Peterborough?
173	B.10.5 (216)	[with London, B.L. Cotton Vitellius C.viii, fols. 85-90] Epistolae Pauli, incomplete, with gloss (partly from Pelagius) : s. viii^1, prob. Northumbria, (prov. Durham).
174	B.11.2 (241)	Amalarius, *Liber officialis* (Retractatio prima ; with glosses s. x^2 - xi^1) : s. x$^{2/4}$ (930s) or x med., Canterbury StA. Additions : Antiphon (s. xi^1) ; *Dies Aegyptiaci* ; Excerpts from Amalarius, *Liber officialis* ; Donation inscription$^+$* : s. xi$^{3/4}$, Exeter, whole MS prov. Exeter.
175	B.14.3 (289)	Arator, *Historia apostolica*, with scholia (by 'Anonymus X') ; Dunstan, (part of) Acrostic poem (SK 10972) : s. x/xi, Canterbury CC.
175.1	B.14.3 (289), flyleaves 1-4	Ambrose, *Expositio de psalmo CXVIII* (f) : s. ix^1 or ix med., Nonantola, prov. England s. xi, (prov. prob. Canterbury CC).
175.5	B.14.30 (315)	fols. 1-57 : Nine sermons (four erroneously attrib. to Augustine) ; Odilo of Cluny, *Sermo* XIV ; Paschasius Radbertus, *De assumptione B.M.V.* ; Lessons on the Life of the Virgin ; Fulbert of Chartres, *Sermo* 4 : s. xi ex. fols. 58-129 : Ambrose, *De virginibus, De viduis, De virginitate, Exhortatio virginitatis* ; Nicetas of Remesiana (?), *De lapsu virginis consecratae* : s. xi ex., (both parts prov. Exeter, prov. Leicester, Augustinian canons).

176	B.15.33 (368)	[? with fragment formerly Weinheim, Sammlung E. Fischer, s.n., lost] Isidore, *Etymologiae*, V.xxxiii - IX.vii : s. x in., S England (Winchester?).
177	B.15.34 (369)	Ælfric, Homilies* : s. xi med., prob. Canterbury CC.
178	B.16.3 (379)	Hrabanus Maurus, *De laudibus s. crucis* : s. x$^{2/4}$ or x med., S or W England.
179	B.16.44 (405)	Decreta Pontificum and Concilia (Lanfranc's Collection) : s. xi^2 (1059×1079), Normandy (Bec?), prov. Canterbury CC ; Papal letters to Lanfranc and *Conversio Berengarii* (in Gregory VII, *Registrum* VI.17a) : s. xi ex. - xii in., Canterbury CC.
180	R.5.22 (717), fols. 72-158	Gregory (Alfred), *Regula pastoralis** ; Note on the Immaculate conception : s. x/xi, prov. Sherborne?, (prov. prob. Salisbury).
181	R.7.5 (743)	Beda, *Historia ecclesiastica* : s. xi in. - xi^2, (prov. prob. N England).
182	R.9.17 (819), fols. 1-48	Ælfric, *Grammar*** (abbrev.) ; Grammatical note** ; *Disticha Catonis** ; Apothegms* : s. xi/xii.
184	R.14.50 (920)	Galen, *Liber tertius* : s. xi med.
185	R.15.14 (939) pt. i	Pseudo-Boethius, *Geometria* I ; Texts and excerpts on geometry and metrology, including excerpts from : Isidore, *Etymologiae*, Hyginus, *De limitibus*, Julius Frontinus, Pseudo-Censorinus, *De geometria*, Cassiodorus, *Institutiones* ii, Euclides latinus ; Epaphroditus et Vitruvius Rufus, Excerpta geometrica ; Balbus, *Ad Celsum expositio et ratio omnium mensurarum* ; Remigius Favius (?), *Carmen de ponderibus et mensuris* (incomplete ; SK 12104) ; *Libellus de mensuris, de ponderibus, de mensuris in liquidis* : s. x^1, N France or Flanders, (prov. Canterbury StA) [cf. no. **185.1**].
185.1	R.15.14 (939) pt. ii	Tonary : s. xi^1, Saint-Vaast, Arras, (prov. England by s. xiii), both **185** and **185.1** in England before 1100?
186	R.15.32 (945)	pp. i, ii, 1-12, 37-218 : *Involutio sphaerae* (extract from Aratus) ; Abbo of Fleury, *De differentia circuli et sphaerae* (pt. ii : '*De cursu septem planetarum*'), *De duplici signorum ortu vel occasu*, (pt. ii : '*De quinque circulis mundi*') ; *Dies Aegyptiaci* ; Hyginus, *Astronomica* ; Martianus Capella, *De nuptiis Philologiae et Mercurii*, bk.viii (part with gloss) ; Helperic, *De computo* ; Abbo of Fleury, *De figuratione signorum* (abbrev. from Hyginus) ; Prayers ; Tract on the stars ; Cicero, *Aratea* (incomplete) : s. xi in. pp. 13-36 : Calendar ; Computus material ('Winchester Computus') : s. xi^1 (1035/6) : whole MS Winchester NM, prov. by s. xi ex. Canterbury StA.

188	O.1.18 (1042)	*Voces animantium* ; Four Latin poems (including SK 16461, 3448, 2652) ; Augustine, *Enchiridion*, glossed ; Dunstan, Acrostic poem (SK 10972) : s. x/xi (or x^2?), Canterbury StA, or Glastonbury?
188.8	O.2.30 (1134), fols. 1-70	Pseudo-Augustine, *De unitate S. Trinitatis* ; Excerpts in dialogue form from Isidore, *Differentiae* and *Etymologiae* ; Isidore, *De fide catholica* : s. xi/xii, (prov. Southwark, Augustinian priory of St. Mary Overy).
189	O.2.30 (1134), fols. 129-172	List of sins ; Introductory poem to Benedictine Rule (doubtfully attrib. to Simplicius, abbot of Monte Cassino ; SK 13285) ; *Regula S. Benedicti*, with gloss ; Four Sermons (s. x/xi) : s. x med., Canterbury StA.
190	O.2.31 (1135)	Prosper, *Epigrammata* and *Versus ad coniugem*, with gloss ; *Disticha Catonis*, with gloss ; Beda, *De die iudicii* ; Prudentius, *Dittochaeon* (all exc. Prosper incomplete) ; Chant in honour of St. Æthelthryth (f ; s. xi) : s. x/xi, Canterbury CC.
191	O.2.51 (1155) pt. i	Prudentius, *Psychomachia* : s. x^2.
192	O.2.51 (1155) pt. ii	Priscian, *Institutiones grammaticae* (bks. i-xviii) ; Priscian (?), *De accentibus* (incomplete) : s. xi/xii., Canterbury (CC?), (prov. Canterbury CC?).
193	O.3.7 (1179)	Boethius, *De consolatione Philosophiae*, with commentary by Remigius (redaction T) ; Lupus of Ferrières, *De metris Boethii* ; Epitaphium Helpis (SK 6193): s. x^2 or x ex., Canterbury StA?, (prov. ibid.).
194	O.3.35 (1207)	Ambrose, *Hexameron* : s. xi/xii, (prov. Chichester Cathedral).
195	O.4.10 (1241)	Juvenal, *Satirae*, with gloss ; 'Cornutus', Commentary on Persius ; Persius, *Satirae*, partly glossed ; Martial, Epigram I.xix : s. $x^{2/4}$, Canterbury StA, (prov. ibid.).
196	O.4.11 (1242)	Hucbald of Saint-Amand, *Ecloga de calvis* ; Juvenal, *Satirae*, with gloss ; Four Latin poems (including SK 638, 2425, 1701) ; Hymn? (SK 14230 ; s. xi) : s. x^2, N France or Flanders, in England before 1100?, (prov. Canterbury StA).
196.5	O.4.34 (1264)	Orosius, *Historiae adversus paganos* ; Julius Honorius (Pseudo-Aethicus), *Cosmographia* (f ; rest in O.4.36, destroyed) : s. xi/xii, Canterbury CC.
198.5	O.10.23 (1475)	Gregory of Tours, *Libri miraculorum* i-vii : s. xi ex., (prov. Exeter).

199	O.10.28 (1480)	Eutropius, *Breviarium*, with additions and continuation by Paulus Diaconus ('*Historia Romana*') : s. xi/xii, Canterbury CC.

200   O.10.31 (1483)   *Inventio s. Crucis* (*BHL* 4169) ; Victor of Vita, *Historia persecutionis Africanae provinciae* : s. xi/xii, Canterbury CC.

200.5   O.11a.5[12]   Aristotle (Boethius), *Categoriae* (f) ; Themistius, *De decem categoriis* (f) : s. ix/x, NE France, in England before 1100?

Cambridge, Trinity Hall

202   24, fols. 78-83   [palimpsest, lower script] Benedictional (f)?, Sacramentary (f)? : s. viii?

Canterbury, Cathedral Library and Archives

204   Lit.A.8 (68)   Augustine and Pseudo-Augustine, 91 Sermons (89 from collection *De verbis Domini et Apostoli*) : s. xi/xii, Canterbury StA.

205.5   Lit.E.28, fols. 1-7   Domesday monachorum : s. xi/xii (after 1089), Canterbury CC.

—   Add. 16   [see no. **448**]

206   Add. 20   Chrodegang, *Regula canonicorum* (enlarged version)⁺* (f) : s. xi³ᐟ⁴, Canterbury CC?, (prov. prob. ibid.).

207   Add. 25   Gregory (Werferth), *Dialogi** (f) : s. x ex., (prov. prob. Canterbury CC).

208   Add. 32   Gregory, *Dialogi* (f) : s. xi in.

209   Add. 127/1   Paulus Diaconus, *Homiliarium* (f) : s. xi¹.

210   Add. 127/12   Homiliarium of Saint-Père, Chartres (f) : s. xi in.

211   Add. 127/19   [with Maidstone, Kent County Archives Office, PRC 49/1a and b] Priscian, *Institutiones grammaticae* (f) : s. ix/x or x¹, prob. N France, prov. prob. Canterbury StA.

212   Add. 128/52   Missal (f) : s. xi med.

212.2   Add. 172   Canticum canticorum ; Epistolae Pauli, with gloss, partly by Lanfranc ; Apocalypsis : s. xi ex., Canterbury StA. [formerly listed as no. **695**].

| 212.3 | Add. 172, fol. 189 | Collectar (f ; or reject leaf) : s. xi med., prov. Canterbury StA. |

| 212.5 | U3/162/28/1 | Augustine, *In Psalmos* (f) : s. xi/xii, Canterbury StA. |

Chichester, Diocesan Record Office

| 212.7 | Ep. I/17/20 | Canticles (f) : s. xi [presumably from a psalter MS]. |

Chichester, West Sussex Record Office

| 212.8 | Cap. I/17/2 | Psalterium Romanum (f ; or reject leaf) : before 780, S England (Selsey?). |

Deene Park Library, near Kettering, Northamptonshire, Trustees of the late Mr. G. Brudenell

| — | L.2.21 | [see no. **648**] |

Dublin, Trinity College

| 213 | 57 (A.4.5) | Gospels : s. vii^2, Northumbria or Iona or Ireland? |

| 214 | 58 (A.1.6) | Gospels : s. viii^2 or viii/ix, Northumbria? Pictland? Iona? Kells? |

| 214.3 | 98 (B.3.6) | Pontifical, Benedictional : s. xi ex., Canterbury CC. FC : Colker (1991), i.195-197. |

| 214.6 | 158 (D.4.15), fol. 94 | Unidentified text (f) : s. x^2. |

| 215 | 174 (B.4.3), fols. 1-44, 52-56, 95-103 | Seventeen Lives of Saints ; Five Homilies for Saints' days (Augustine, Sermones 276, 316, 382, Sermo app. 217 ; Caesarius, Sermo 220) [Companion vol. to nos. **754.5** and **754.6**?] : s. xi ex., Salisbury (supplemented ibid. s. xii in.). FC : Webber (1992), p. 143 ; Colker (1991), i.320-328. |

| 216 | 176 (E.5.28), fols. 1-26 | Goscelin, *Vita S. Æthelburgae, Vita S. Wulfhildae* : s. xi/xii, Barking? |

| 216.3 | 370a | Antiphoner (f) : s. xi^2, Crowland? |

| 216.4 | 371 (D.1.26), pp. i, ii, 149-150 | Gradual (f) : s. xi^2. |

216.6   927   Cicero, *De inventione* : s. xi^2, France or England?

Durham, Cathedral Library

217   A.II.4   Booklist (s. xi/xii) ; Bible, (vol. ii : Prophets - Apocalypse) ; Remigius (Haimo of Auxerre?), Commentary on Apocalypse (abbrev., incomplete) : s. xi ex. (before 1096), Normandy, prov. Durham.

218   A.II.10, fols. 2-5,   [with C.III.13, fols. 192-195, and C.III.20, fols. 1 and 2]
          338, 339   Gospels (or New Testament?) (f) : s. vii med., Northumbria (or Ireland?), prov. prob. Chester-le-Street, prov. Durham.

219   A.II.16   [with Cambridge, Magdalene College, Pepys 2981 (18)]
         Gospels: s. viii, Northumbria, prov. prob. Chester-le-Street, prov. Durham.

220   A.II.17,   [with Cambridge, Magdalene College, Pepys 2981 (19)]
         fols. 2-102   Gospels (incomplete) ; Poem on King Æthelstan (SK 2143 ; s. x/xi) : s. vii ex. or viii in., Northumbria, prob. Lindisfarne, prov. Chester-le-Street, prov. Durham.

221   A.II.17,   Gospel of St. Luke (f) : s. vii/viii, Wearmouth-J., prov. Chester-
         fols. 103-111   le-Street, prov. Durham.

222   A.III.29   Paulus Diaconus, *Homiliarium* (Temporale : Easter to 25th Sunday after Whitsun ; Sanctorale : May to Dec.) [Companion vol. to no. **226**, and cf. no. **249.3**] : s. xi ex. (before 1096), Durham.
                             FC : Rud (1825), pp. 45-56.

222.3   A.III.31, fols.   Medical text : s. x ex.
         1-4, 288-291

222.8   A.IV.16, fols.   Augustine, *De Genesi ad litteram* (incomplete) : s. xi/xii, Durham.
         66-109

223   A.IV.19   Collectar°, Texts from pontifical services° : s. ix/x, S England, prov. Chester-le-Street ; Texts for Mass and Office° ; Prayers° ; List of *notae juris*° ; (Various notes :) On Adam's creation° ; On the nature of the winds° ; On Roman imperial dignitaries° ; On titles of kings° ; *De ecclesiae gradibus*° ; On the burial-places of the Apostles ; OE gloss to all texts : s. x^2, Chester-le-Street, prov. whole MS Durham.
                             FC : *Rituale Ecclesiae Dunelmensis*, ed. A. H. Thompson and U. Lindelöf, Surtees Soc. 140 (1927) ; *The Durham Collectar*, ed. A Corrêa, HBS 107 (1992).

224   A.IV.19, fol. 89   Mass lectionary (f) : s. viii, Northumbria.

225	A.IV.28	Beda, *In Apocalypsin* : s. xi/xii or xii in., (prov. Durham).
225.5	B.II.1	Josephus, *Antiquitates Judaicae* (Latin version), *De bello Judaico* (version by 'Hegesippus') : s. xi/xii, (prov. Durham).
226	B.II.2	Paulus Diaconus, *Homiliarium* (orig. Advent to Easter, now incomplete : Christmas to Good Friday) [Companion vol. to no. **222** and cf. no. **249.3**] : s. xi ex. (before 1096), Durham. FC : Rud (1825), pp. 93-97.
227	B.II.6	Ambrose, *De Joseph patriarcha*, *De patriarchis*, *De paenitentia*, *De excessu fratris*, *De bono mortis*, *De obitu Valentiniani*, *De paradiso* (incomplete), *De Abraham patriarcha* (bk.i only), *De Nabuthae* ; Augustine, *De decem chordis* (*Sermo* 9 ; s. xi/xii) : s. xi ex. (before 1096), (prov. Durham).
228	B.II.9	Jerome, *In Prophetas minores* : s. xi ex. (before 1096), Normandy, prov. Durham.
229	B.II.10, fols. 1-183	Jerome, *Epistolae* (includes pseudonymous letter and letters to Jerome) ; Origenes (Jerome), *In Canticum canticorum* ; Jerome, *Adversus Helvidium*, *Contra Vigilantium* : s. xi ex. (before 1096), Canterbury CC, prov. Durham.
230	B.II.11	fols. 1-108 : Jerome, *Hebraicae quaestiones in Genesin*, Eusebius (Jerome), *De situ et nominibus locorum Hebraicorum*, Jerome, *Liber interpretationis Hebraicorum nominum*, *Epistola* 125 (122?) *ad Rusticum* ; Pseudo-Jerome, *Interpretatio alphabeti Hebraeorum* (and explanation of Greek alphabet), *Hebraicae quaestiones in Libros Regum*, in *Paralipomena*, *Decem temptationes populi Israel*, *De sex civitatibus ad quas homicida fugit*, *In Canticum Deborae*, *In Lamentationes Hieremiae*, *Super aedificium Prudentii*, *Epistolae supp.* 23, 44, 45, *De sphaera caeli* ; Jerome (?), *Notae divinae legis necessariae* ; texts, excerpts and short verse compositions (including W 12589, 14969, 11179) dealing with the etymology of Hebrew names, with science (computus, geometry, metals, stones) and with music, including excerpt from Guido of Arezzo, *Micrologus* ; Excerpt from *Liber Pontificalis* : s. xi ex. (before 1096), Normandy, prov. Durham. fols. 109-137 : Fulbert of Chartres, *Epistolae*, Treatises, *Sermones* 1, 7 and 8, Poems ; Robert II of France and Gauzlin, Letters : s. xi ex. (before 1096), Normandy, prov. Durham.
231	B.II.13	Augustine, *In Psalmos* (51-100) [Companion vol. to no. **232**] : s. xi ex. (before 1096), Normandy, prov. Durham.
232	B.II.14	Augustine, *In Psalmos* (101-150) [Companion vol. to no. **231**] : s. xi ex., Normandy, prov. Durham.

233	B.II.16	Augustine, *In Evangelium Johannis* : s. xi ex., Canterbury StA, prov. Durham before 1100?, (prov. Durham).
234	B.II.17	Augustine, *In Evangelium Johannis* : s. xi ex. (before 1096), Normandy, prov. Durham.
235	B.II.21, fols. 9-158	Augustine, *Epistolae* (and letters to Augustine), and additions (s. xi/xii) : s. xi ex. (before 1096), Durham.
236	B.II.22, fols. 27-231	Augustine, *De civitate Dei* , with *Retractatio* II.xliii ; Lanfranc's notes on *De civitate Dei* and (add. s. xi/xii) on the translations of Plato's *Timaeus* ; Grammatical notes (s. xi/xii) : s. xi ex. (before 1096), Durham (or N France?), or Canterbury StA, prov. Durham.
237	B.II.30	Cassiodorus, *In Psalmos* (breviate version) : s. viii$^{2/4}$, Northumbria (York?), (prov. Durham) ; fols. 3-4 and 265 supply leaves s. xi/xii.
238	B.II.35, fols. 38-118	Beda, *Historia ecclesiastica* : s. xi ex. (before 1096), Normandy or England, (prov. Durham).
239	B.III.1	Origenes, *Homiliae in Vetus Testamentum* (in Latin : Homilies on Genesis, Exodus, Leviticus, Josua, Judices, I Reges trans. Rufinus ; Homilies on Canticum canticorum, Isaias, Hieremias, Ezechiel trans. Jerome) ; Rufinus, *De benedictionibus patriarcharum* (excerpt) : s. xi ex. (before 1096), Normandy, prov. Durham.
240	B.III.9	Gregory (?), *Symbolum fidei* ; Gregory, *Registrum epistolarum* : s. xi ex., (prov. Durham).
241	B.III.10	Gregory, *Moralia*, bks. 1-16 : s. xi ex. (before 1096), Normandy, prov. Durham.
241.3	B.III.10, fol. ii	Unidentified sermon (f) : s. xi/xii.
241.5	B.III.10, fols. 1 bis and 243	Breviary (f) : s. xi ex. or xii in., prob. Normandy, prov. Durham.
—	B.III.10, fols. 239 and 242	[see no. **243.5**]
242	B.III.11, fols. 1-135	Gregory, *Homiliae in Evangelia* ; Homilies (most as in Haimo of Auxerre, *Homiliarium*) : s. xi ex., Continent (Liège?), prov. Durham. FC : Rud (1825), pp. 156-158.
242.5	B.III.11, fols. 136-159	Antiphoner : s. xi ex., Liège, (prov. Durham). FC : R. J. Hesbert, *Corpus Antiphonalium Officii* (Rome, 1963-79).

243	B.III.16	Hrabanus Maurus, *In Matthaeum*, with introductory poem (SK 9447) : s. xi ex. (before 1096), Normandy, prov. Durham.
243.5	B.III.16, fols. 159 and 160	[with B.III.10, fols. 239 and 242] Augustine, *Sermones* (f) : s. xi ex., Normandy, prov. Durham.
244	B.III.32	Hymnal°, Monastic canticles° : s. xi$^{2/4}$; Proverbs^{+*} : s. xi med. ; Ælfric, *Grammar*$^{+*}$; Dialogue on declinations : s. xi^{1} or xi med. ; whole MS Canterbury, prob. CC (StA?). FC : I. B. Milfull, *The Hymns of the Anglo-Saxon Church*, CSASE 17 (Cambridge, 1996) ; Korhammer (1976).
245	B.IV.6, fol. 169*	Bible (f ; from I Macchabaei) : s. vi, Italy, prov. Northumbria.
246	B.IV.9	Gennadius, On Prudentius (*De viris illustribus*, ch. xiii) ; Prudentius, *Praefatio, Cathemerinon, Apotheosis, Hamartigenia, Psychomachia, Peristephanon, Contra Symmachum, Dittochaeon, Epilogus*, all glossed ; Optatianus Porfyrius, *carm.* 15 (SK 605) : s. x med., (prov. Durham).
246.8	B.IV.12, fols. 1-120	fols. 1-38 : Fulgentius of Ruspe, *Epistola ad Donatum* (*Epist.* 8), *De fide ad Petrum* ; Gennadius, *Liber ecclesiasticorum dogmatum* ; Augustine, *De utilitate agendae paenitentiae* (*Sermo* 351), *De paenitentibus* (*Sermo* 393) : s. xi/xii. fols. 39-120 : Prosper, *De gratia Dei, Pro Augustino responsiones ad capitula obiectionum Gallorum, Responsiones ad capitula obiectionum Vincentianarum, Responsiones ad excerpta Genuensium* ; Augustine, *De octo Dulcitii quaestionibus, Sermo* 200; Pseudo-Augustine, *Hypomnesticon* bk.vi, *Sermones app.* 121, 128, 138 ; Ambrose, *De mysteriis, De Spiritu Sancto* (prologue), *De apologia prophetae David* ; Pseudo-Augustine and Pseudo-Jerome, *De essentia divinitatis* : s. xi/xii or xii in., both parts Durham.
247	B.IV.13	Gregory, *Homiliae in Ezechielem* : s. xi ex. (before 1096), prov. Durham.
248	B.IV.24	fol. 5 : Confraternity conventions : s. xi ex., Durham. fols. 6-11 : Calendar, with obits but no saints' feasts : s. xi ex. fols. 12-45 : Martyrologium (Usuard), with obits ; Gospel lectionary for use in the Chapter Office (with gospels abbreviated?) : s. xi ex. fols. 47-71 : Lanfranc, *Constitutiones* : s. xi ex. (1091×1096), Canterbury CC. fol. 74 : William of St. Carilef, Letter : s. xi/xii. fols. 74-123 : *Regula S. Benedicti*$^{+*}$: s. xi^{2} or xi/xii. fols. 126-127 : Liturgical and other notes : s. xi/xii. All parts prov. Durham s. xi/xii (by 1096) ; numerous later additions, esp. obits.

—	C.III.13, fols. 192-195	[see no. **218**]
—	C.III.20, fols. 1 and 2	[see no. **218**]
249	C.IV.7, flyleaves	Bible (f ; from Leviticus xiv, xv, xxvi) : s. viii, prob. Northumbria.
249.3	C.IV.12, binding strips	*Homiliarium* (f) [from Companion vol. to nos. **222** and **226**?] : s. xi ex., Durham.

Durham, Dean and Chapter Muniments

250	Misc. Charter 5670	Psalterium Gallicanum (f) : s. xi^1.

Durham, University Library

251	Cosin V.v.6	Gradual with Kyriale ; *Laudes regiae* ; add. sequences (s. xi/xii) : s. xi$^{4/4}$ or xi ex., Canterbury CC, prov. Durham.

Edinburgh, National Library of Scotland

Advocates

251.5	18.4.3, fols. 1-122	'Heraclides', *Paradisus* (trans. from Palladius, *Historia Lausiaca*) ; Victor of Vita, *Historia persecutionis Africanae provinciae* ; Paschasius Radbertus, *De corpore et sanguine Domini* ; Augustine, *De sacramentis altaris* (*Sermo* 52) : s. xi ex., (prov. Durham).
252	18.6.12	Persius, *Satirae* ; Latin epigram (SK 14414) ; Avianus, *Fabulae* ; *Cato novus* (incomplete) ; Latin poetic fragment (SK 9929) ; *Gesta Ludovici imperatoris* (incomplete ; SK 3866) ; Verse excerpts from Horace, *Epistolae* ; Three Latin poems (W 11654, 13383 ; 14284 by Marbod of Rennes) ; Three Latin epigrams and three riddles ; Abbo of Saint-Germain, *Bella Parisiacae urbis*, bk.iii ; Symphosius, *Aenigmata* (incomplete) : s. xi ex. or xii in., (prov. Thorney).
253	18.7.7	Sedulius, Letter I to Macedonius, *Carmen paschale*°, Hymns ; Four poems on Sedulius (SK 15784, 14842, 14841, 12954), one by Pseudo- Vergil (SK 16845): s. x ex., OE glosses partly s. xi, (prov. Thorney).

254   18.7.8   [palimpsest, upper writing]
Cicero, *In Catilinam* i-iv ; (Pseudo?-)Sallust and Pseudo-Cicero, *Invectivae* ; Atticus (?), *Epistola formata* ; Greek letters explained : s. xi ex., (prov. Thorney).

255   18.7.8   [palimpsest, lower script, fragments]
fols. 1?, 4, 5, 8?, 9, 16, 28, 31 : Augustine, *De Trinitate* : s. viii ;
fols. 12, 13, 23, 30 : Service-book, prob. sacramentary : s. xi in. ;
fols. 19, 22 : *Passio S. Laurentii* (*BHL* 4754) : s. viii[1] ;
fols. 26, 33 : Gregory, *Homiliae in Evangelia* : s. viii ex. ;
fols. 27, 32 and fols. in 18.6.12 : unidentified writing.

Edinburgh, University Library

255.5   56 (D.b.III.8)   Psalterium Hebraicum : s. xi[1], Ireland or Scotland, in Scotland or England by s. xi[2].

Eton College

—   220, no.1   [see no. **669**]

Exeter, Cathedral Library

256   3500   Exon Domesday : c. 1086, prob. Salisbury, (prov. Exeter).

—   3501, fols. 0-7   [see no. **15**]

257   3501, fols. 8-130   OE Poetry : *Christ** ; *Guthlac** ; *Azarias** ; *Phoenix** ; *Juliana** ; *Wanderer** ; *Seafarer** ; *Widsith** ; Maxims* ; *Riming Poem** ; *Panther*, *Whale** and *Partridge** ; *Soul and Body** ; *Deor** ; *Wulf and Eadwacer** ; Riddles* ; *Wife's Lament** ; *Judgement Day I** ; *Husband's Message** ; *Ruin** ; other shorter poems* : s. x[2], prob. SW England (or Canterbury CC??), prov. Exeter by s. xi[3/4].

258   3507   Hrabanus Maurus, *De computo* ; Verses (SK 7632 = Vergil, *Georg.* i.231-9 ; 6489 ; 12559, by Ausonius ; 3727, 12524, 1716, 8931, 12491) and prose notes mainly on computus subjects ; Greek, Hebrew and three runic alphabets ; Isidore, *De natura rerum* : s. x[2], S England (Canterbury CC or Sherborne?), prov. Exeter s. xi[2].

258.3   3512   Decreta Pontificum (Lanfranc's Collection) [Companion vol. to no. **601.5**] : s. xi ex., Exeter?, (prov. ibid.)

258.8   3548A   Missal (f) : s. x[1], N France or Brittany, prov. Exeter possibly s. xi[2].

259	3548C	Benedictional (f) : s. x^2 or x ex., Winchester?, prov. s. xi prob. Exeter.
259.5	FMS/1,2,2a	Orosius, *Historiae adversus paganos* (f) : s. x^1, N France?
260	FMS/3	*Vita S. Basilii* (f ; *BHL* 1023) : s. x in. or x^1, England, (prov. Exeter).

Glasgow, University Library

261	Hunterian 431 (V.5.1), fols. 1-102	Gregory, *Regula pastoralis* (fols. 103-158 supplied s. xii in.) : s. x/xi or xi in., (prov. Worcester).

Gloucester, Cathedral Library

262	35	Ælfric, Homilies* (f) ; Lives of Saints* (f) : s. xi^1 ; Life of St. Mary of Egypt* (f) : s. xi med. ; *Regula S. Benedicti*, ch. 4* (f) : s. xi^2, (prov. Gloucester all fragments).

Hereford Cathedral Library

263	O.III.2	Jerome, *De viris illustribus* ; *Decretum* (Pseudo-)*Gelasianum de libris recipiendis* ; Gennadius, and Isidore, *De viris illustribus* ; Augustine, *Retractatio* ; Cassiodorus, *Institutiones*, bk.i ; Isidore, *Prooemia Veteris et Novi Testamenti* , *De ecclesiasticis officiis* (excerpts), *De ortu et obitu patrum, Allegoriae sacrae Scripturae* ; excerpt from a grammarian 'Terrentius' : s. ix^2, France, prov. England (Salisbury?) s. xi ex., (prov. Hereford by s. xii med.).
263.5	O.III.6, fol. 1	Sacramentary (f) : s. x ex., (prov. Hereford, Franciscans).
264	O.VI.11	Paschasius Radbertus, *De assumptione B. M. V.* ; Jerome, *Epistolae* 39, 31, 54, 22 ; ('Martinellus') : Sulpicius Severus, *Vita S. Martini*, *Epistolae* I and III ; Gregory of Tours, Excerpts from *De virtutibus S. Martini* and *Historia Francorum, Vita S. Bricii* (from *Historia Francorum*, II.1) ; Sulpicius Severus, *Dialogi* II, III, I ; Guitmund of Aversa, *Confessio de S. Trinitate* ; Odo of Glanfeuil (Pseudo-Faustus), *Vita S. Mauri* ; Two responsories (added ; including W 12877a) : s. xi ex., (prov. Hereford, St. Guthlac's Priory).
265	O.VIII.8	Decreta Pontificum and Concilia (Lanfranc's Collection) : s. xi ex., prov. Hereford.
265.5	O.IX.2	Bible (part of Old Testament : I-IV Regum, Isaias, Hieremias, Ezechiel, Daniel, Minor prophets) : s. xi ex.

266	P.I.2	Gospels (incomplete) ; Records* (s. xi med.) : s. viii med., W Midlands or Wales, prov. Hereford s. xi[1].
266.5	P.I.10	Didymus (Jerome), *De Spiritu Sancto* ; Pseudo-Orosius and Pseudo-Augustine, *Dialogus quaestionum LXV* ; Vigilius Thapsensis, *Contra Felicianum* ; Augustine, *De orando Deo (Epist.* 130), *Sermo* 37, *De octo Dulcitii quaestionibus* ; Two anonymous short texts : s. xi/xii, W England.
267	P.II.5, fols. 1-145	'Heraclides', *Paradisus* (trans. from Palladius, *Historia Lausiaca*) ; Leontius (Anastasius Bibliothecarius), *Vita Johannis Eleemosynarii* (both from *Vitas Patrum*) ; Johannes Diaconus, *Vita S. Nicholai* : s. xi[2].
268	P.II.10, fols. i and 61	Pseudo-Alcuin, *Liber quaestionum in Evangeliis* (f, from Matthew) : s. viii, prob. Northumbria.
268.2	P.V.1, fols. 1-28	Lanfranc, *Constitutiones* ; Vigilius Thapsensis, *Contra Felicianum* : s. xi/xii or xii in., Battle?, (prov. ibid.).
268.4	P.VI.1, fol. 177	Prayerbook? (f) : s. x[2].

Hertford, Hertfordshire Record Office

268.6	Gorehambury X.D.4.B and X.D.4.C	Office lectionary (f) : s. xi[2], prov. St. Albans?

Kingston Lacy, Dorset, National Trust

—	[see no. **501.3**]

Langley Marish, Buckinghamshire, Parish Church

—	[see no. **501**]

Leeds, University Library

—	[see no. **696**]

Lichfield, Cathedral Library

269 1 Gospels (incomplete) : s. viii$^{2/4}$ or viii med., W Midlands or Northumbria?, prov. Wales (prob. Llandeilo Fawr, Carmarthenshire) s. ix, prov. Lichfield prob. s. x^1 ; Welsh, Latin and Old English marginalia s. viii/ix - xi^1.

269.1 1a Boethius, *In categorias Aristotelis* (f) ; Aristoteles (Boethius), *De interpretatione* (f) : s. x^2, France?

Lincoln, Cathedral Library

270 1 (A.1.2) [with Trinity College, Cambridge, B.5.2 : a two-volume Bible] Lincoln : Old Testament (Genesis - Job) ; Psalterium Gallicanum (incomplete). Trinity : Old Testament (Proverbia - Libri Macchabaeorum) ; New Testament (Epistolae incomplete). Both vols. s. xi ex. or xi/xii, E England (Lincoln?), prov. Lincoln.

271 13 (A.1.26) Augustine, *De Genesi ad litteram* with *Retractatio* I.xviii, *De Genesi contra Manichaeos* ; Pseudo-Orosius and Pseudo-Augustine, *Dialogus quaestionum LXV* : s. xi ex. or xi/xii, (prov. Lincoln).

272 106 (A.4.14) Extracts from Concilia in Lanfranc's Collection (*Canones Apostolorum* ; Four Councils ; Atticus (?), *Epistola formata*) ; Gregory the Great, *Epist.* I.24, V.18, IV.26 ; Greek alphabet : s. xi ex. or xi/xii, Normandy or England?

273 158 (C.2.2) Paulus Diaconus, *Homiliarium* (beginning of Lent to Easter vigil, Sanctorale 25. Jan. - 30. Nov., Commune SS.) : s. xi ex., Normandy or England. FC : R. M. Thomson, *Catalogue of the Manuscripts of Lincoln Cathedral Chapter Library* (Woodbridge, 1989), pp. 124-127.

274 182 (C.2.8) [with 184, fol. 1] Beda, *Homiliae in Evangelia* : s. x/xi, Abingdon, (prov. Lincoln).

— 184 (C.1.13), fol. 1 [see no. **274**]

275 298A Gospels (f) : s. viii^2, Northumbria.

276 298B Hexateuch* (f ; from Numeri) : s. xi^2.

277 298C [with London, B.L. Harley 3405, fol. 4] Antiphoner (f) : s. xi med.

57

— V.5.11 (ptd. bk.)   [see no. **524**]

Lincoln, Dean and Chapter Muniments

277.3   A/2/20/2   Lectionary (f) : s. xi med.

London, British Library (until 1973 British Museum)

– Additional

278   7138   On Anglo-Saxon bishoprics : s. x^2 ; Canterbury StA? or Crediton or Exeter.

279   9381   Gospels, Gospel list : s. ix/x, Brittany ; Records$^{(*)}$: s. x med. - xi/xii, prov. whole MS s. x St. Petroc's, Padstow, then Bodmin.

280   11034   Beda, *De die iudicii* (part) ; Pseudo-Priscian, *Carmen de sideribus* ; Arator, *Historia apostolica* with scholia (by 'Anonymus X') ; Modoin of Autun, *Ecloga* (for Charlemagne) : s. x?, prob. England.

281   15350, fols. 1   *Verba seniorum* xiii.9 - xiv.1, 10-17 (*Vitas Patrum* bk.V) : s. vii-viii,
and 121   prob. Italy, (prov. Winchester OM).

281.3   19835   Heiric of Auxerre, *Collectanea* (from Suetonius, Orosius, Valerius Maximus) ; Theological treatises ; Treatise on Greek alphabet ; Fulbert of Chartres, *Epistolae*, two sermons ; Liturgical directions and expositions ; Excerpts from Jerome and Augustine on the psalms ; Interpretations of biblical names (f) : s. xi/xii, Normandy or England.

281.5   21213,   [Palimpsest ; lower script]
fols. 2-25   Gospels (f) : s. viii ex., prob. England.

282   23211   Computistical verses and note ; Genealogies of West-Saxon and East-Saxon kings* ; Old English Martyrology* (f) : c. 871×899, Wessex.

283   23944   Augustine, *De nuptiis et concupiscentia, Contra Julianum* : s. $ix^{3/4}$, prob. Paris-Beauvais region, prov. England s. xi ex., (prov. Burton-upon-Trent).

284   24193   Venantius Fortunatus, *Carmina* : s. ix^1, France (Orléans area?), prov. England s. $x^{3/4}$; fols. 1-16 and 159 replacement leaves, England s. $x^{3/4}$.

285   24199,   Prudentius, *Psychomachia* with glosses : s. x ex. ; some drawings
fols. 2-38   s. xi^2, xi/xii, (prov. Bury St. Edmunds).

286	28188	Pontifical, Benedictional : s. x$^{3/4}$, Exeter.

—   32246   [see no. **775**]

287   33241   *Encomium Emmae Reginae* : s. xi med., Flanders (Saint-Omer?) or Normandy, (prov. Canterbury StA).

—   34652, fol. 2   [see no. **357**]

288   34652, fol. 3   Chrodegang, *Regula canonicorum* (enlarged version)$^{+}$* (f) : s. xi^{2}.

289   34652, fol. 6   Bible (f ; from Canticum canticorum, capitula for Sapientia) : s. xi/xii.

290   34890   Gospels, Gospel list : s. xi$^{1/4}$, Canterbury CC, prov. Winchester NM ; Letter by Fulk of Rheims to King Alfred : s. xi ex., Winchester NM.

291   37517   Calendar (s. x/xi) ; Psalterium Romanum° ; Canticles° ; Litany (s. x/xi or xi in.) ; Prayers ; Hymnal ; Monastic canticles : s. x$^{3/4}$, OE glosses s. xi in.; Ordinary and canon of the Mass ; Mass of the Holy Trinity ; part of Office of the Dead : s. x/xi ; whole MS Canterbury (CC?).
FC : G. R. Wieland, ed., *The Canterbury Hymnal* (Toronto, 1982) ; Korhammer (1976); *ASM* 2, pp. 3-11.

292   37518, fols. 116-117   Sacramentary (f) : s. viii^{1}.

293   37777   [with Add. 45025 and prob. B.L. Loan 81 ; cf. no. **501.3**]
Bible (f ; from Libri Regum and Ecclesiasticus) : s. vii ex. or viii in., Wearmouth-J., prov. Worcester?

294   38651, fols. 57 and 58   Sermon notes* : s. xi in., before 1023, Worcester or York.

295   40000   Gospels : s. x in., France, prob. Brittany, or SW France? ; Pericope notes : s. x/xi, England ; Liber vitae (Confraternity lists) : s. xi/xii and later, Thorney, prov. Thorney by 1100.

296   40074   ('Martinellus') : Sulpicius Severus, *Vita S. Martini, Epistolae, Dialogi* ; Pseudo-Sulpicius, *Tituli metrici de S. Martino* (SK 17053); Note on the basilica at Tours ; Symbolum 'Clemens Trinitas' : s. x/xi, Canterbury (CC or StA?).

297   40165 A.1   Cyprian, *Epistolae* (f) : s. iv ex., Africa?

298   40165 A.2   Old English Martyrology* (f) : s. ix ex. or ix/x.

299	40618	Gospels : s. viii², Ireland, prov. s. x med. S England (Canterbury StA?).
299.5	43405, fols. i and v	Missal (f) : s. xi¹, (prov. Muchelney?).
—	45025	[see no. **293**]
—	46204	[see no. **344.5**]
300	47967	Orosius, *Historiae adversus paganos** ; Note* on Adam, Noah, and Old Testament figures (s. xi) : s. x¹ or x²ᐟ⁴, Winchester?
301	49598	Benedictional with prefatory poem by Godeman (SK 12366) : 971×984, Winchester, prob. OM. FC : G. F. Warner and H. A. Wilson, *The Benedictional of St Æthelwold*, Roxburghe Club (Oxford, 1910) ; A. Prescott in *Bishop Æthelwold*, ed. B. Yorke (Woodbridge, 1988), pp. 128-131.
—	50843 K	[see no. **857**]
301.5	56488, fols. i-iii, 1-5	Breviary (f) : s. xi¹, (prov. Muchelney?).
302	57337	Pontifical ; Benedictional (incomplete) : s. x/xi (or 1020s?), Canterbury CC (or Winchester OM?). FC : Prescott (1987), pp. 134-138.
302.2	61735	Farming Memoranda : 1007×1025, Ely.
—	62104	[see no. **524**]
302.3	63143	Gospels (f) : s. x/xi.
302.4	63651	Prayers (f ; from service-book?) : s. xi in.
—	71687	[see no. **857**]

– Arundel

303	16	Osbern, *Vita S. Dunstani* : s. xi/xii, Canterbury CC, (prov. Dover).
304	60	Lunarium for blood-letting ; Calendar ; Computus material ('Winchester Computus') ; Psalterium Gallicanum° ; Canticles° ; Litany ; Prayers : s. xi², prob. 1073 ; Added prayers s. xi ex. ; Six Ages of the World⁺* ; List of bishops of Winchester : c. 1099 ; whole MS Winchester NM.

305.5	125	Job, Esdra : s. ix[1], NE France (prob. Saint-Bertin), prov. England by s. x/xi.
306	155, fols. 1-135 and 171-191	Calendar ; Computus material ; Psalterium Romanum (extensively corrected to Gallicanum, s. xi[2]) ; Canticles ; Prayers° : 1012×1023, Canterbury CC ; OE gloss, Gloria, Creeds, Pater noster add. ibid. s. xi med.
306.5	235	Hugo of Langres, Commentary on the Psalms ; Explanation of the Hebrew alphabet ; Hymn incipit (SK 17048) : s. xi ex.

– Burney

307	277, fol. 42	Laws : *Ine** (f) : s. xi[2], SE England.
307.2	277, fols. 69-72	[with London, B.L. Stowe 1061, fol. 125] Antiphoner (f) : s. xi in. or xi[1], Canterbury CC (Exeter?).

– Cotton

307.4	Augustus II.18	Letter of Bishop Wealdhere : 704 or 705, S England.
307.6	Augustus II.36	Survey of lands in Kent : 1072×1086, Canterbury CC.
307.8	Augustus II.56	Decree of the Council of Clofesho (803) : s. ix[1].
308	Caligula A.vii	*Heliand* (in Old Saxon) ; Charm* (s. xi[1]) : s. x[2], S England.
308.2	Caligula A.viii, fols. 121-128	*Vita S. Birini* (f ; *BHL* 1361) ; Wulfstan of Winchester, *Vita S. Æthelwoldi* (f) : s. xi/xii or xii in., Winchester OM, (prov. Ely).
309	Caligula A.xiv, fols. 1-36	Troper : s. xi[3/4], prob. Winchester or Worcester, (prov. Worcester). FC : Frere (1894) ; Planchart (1977).
310	Caligula A.xiv, fols. 93-130	Ælfric, Lives of St. Martin* and St. Thomas* ; Life of St. Mildred* : s. xi med.
311	Caligula A.xv, fols. 3-117	Jerome, *De viris illustribus*, *Vita S. Pauli Eremitae* ; Isidore, *Etymologiae*, I.xxi-xxvii ; Cyprian, *Ad Quirinum Testimonia*, bk.iii ; Cassiodorus, (?) *De computo paschali* ; Computus texts : s. viii[2] with s. ix[1] and ix/x additions, NE France, prov. England by s. ix/x.
—	Caligula A.xv, fols. 120-153	[see no. **411**]

312	Claudius A.i, fols. 5-36	Frithegod, *Breviloquium Vitae Wilfridi*, glossed : s. x med., Canterbury CC? Glosses s. x^2, (prov. Glastonbury?).
—	Claudius A.iii, fols. 2-7 and 9*	[see no. **362**]
313	Claudius A.iii, fols. 9-18 and 87-105	Pontifical (incomplete) : s. $xi^{2/4}$ or xi med., prob. Canterbury CC. FC : Turner (1971), pp. 89-113.
314	Claudius A.iii, fols. 31-86 and 106-150	Metrical inscription* ; Laws : *Æthelred VI*** (s. $xi^{1/4}$) ; Pontifical ; Benedictional : s. x/xi, Worcester or York. FC : Turner (1971), pp. 1-88.
315	Claudius B.iv	Hexateuch* (part trans. Ælfric) : s. $xi^{2/4}$, Canterbury StA?, (prov. ibid.).
316	Claudius B.v	Acts of the Council of Constantinople (680) : s. ix^1, W Germany, prov. England (royal court) by s. x^1, prov. Bath s. x^1.
316.1	Claudius B.v, fol. 132^v	Gospels or gospel lectionary (f) : c. 800, Court of Charlemagne (miniature pasted onto fol. 132^v of no. **316**).
317	Claudius C.vi, fols. 8-169	Burchard of Worms, *Decretum* : s. xi med. (after 1049), Continent, (prov. Canterbury CC?).
319	Cleopatra A.iii	Three glossaries⁺* : s. $x^{2/4}$ or x med., Canterbury StA.
320	Cleopatra A.iii*	Augustine, *De consensu Evangelistarum* (f) : s. viii^2, Northumbria? S England (Kent)?, prov. Canterbury StA s. x?
321	Cleopatra A.vi, fols. 2-53	Donatus, *Ars maior* ; A 'parsing grammar' ; Two grammatical treatises ; Johannes Diaconus (?), Poem about Gregory the Great (SK 5725) : s. x, prob. x med., W England or Wales?
321.5	Cleopatra A.vii, fols. 107-147	Helperic, *De computo* ; Short computus text : s. xi ex. or xi/xii.
322	Cleopatra B.xiii, fols. 1-58	Homilies* ; Coronation oath* ; Ælfric's translations of Pater noster* and Creed* : s. $xi^{3/4}$, Exeter [one vol. with no. **520**? Companion vol. to no. **109**, pp. 3-98 and 209-224?].
323	Cleopatra B.xiii, fols. 59-90	*Vita S. Dunstani* by 'B' (*BHL* 2342) ; Responsory : s. xi in. or xi^1, Canterbury StA?, (prov. ibid.)
324	Cleopatra C.viii, fols. 4-37	Prudentius, *Psychomachia* ; Pseudo-Columbanus, *Praecepta vivendi* (f) : s. x/xi, Canterbury CC.

325	Cleopatra D.i, fols. 1-82	Vitruvius, *De architectura* ; *Epitaphium Vitalis* (SK 13567) : s. xi^1, (prov. Canterbury StA).
325.1	Cleopatra D.i, fols. 83-128	Vegetius, *Epitome rei militaris* : s. xi^1, Continent?, (prov. Canterbury StA). In England before 1100?
326	Domitian i, fols. 2-55	Beda, *De natura rerum*, ch. 2 ; Isidore, *De natura rerum* : s. x^2 ; Glossary to Abbo, *Bella Parisiacae urbis*, and Priscian, *Institutio* ; Computus material (incomplete) : s. xi/xii ; Priscian, *Institutio de nomine, pronomine et verbo*, with commentary by Remigius ; Beda, *De die iudicii* : s. x med. ; Medical recipe*, Booklist* : s. x^2, x/xi, all parts prob. Canterbury StA, (prov. ibid.).
327	Domitian vii, fols. 15-45 (and added fols.)	*Liber Vitae* : c. 840, Lindisfarne or Wearmouth-J.?, prov. s. ix ex. Chester-le-Street, prov. s. x ex. Durham ; Additions from s. $ix^{2/4}$; Records* add. s. x ex. and xi med.
328	Domitian viii, fols. 30-70	*Anglo-Saxon Chronicle* F^+* : s. xi/xii, Canterbury CC.
329	Domitian ix, fols. 2-7	Aldhelm, *Epistola ad Heahfridum* : s. x in. or x^1, Canterbury CC.
329.5	Domitian ix, fol. 8	Alphabets ; Glossary (f) ; Dionysius Exiguus, *Epistola de ratione Paschae* (f) : s. viii^2, possibly England.
329.9	Domitian ix, fol. 10	[see no. **22**]
330	Domitian ix, fol. 11	Extracts from Beda, *Historia ecclesiastica** ; Runic alphabet (with s. xi/xii add.) : s. ix ex. (after 883) or x in., SE England? London, St. Paul's?
330.5	Faustina A.v, fols. 99-102	Pseudo-Jerome (Pseudo-Beda), *De quindecim signis ante diem iudicii* ; Pseudo-Augustine, *De Antichristo quomodo et ubi nasci debeat* : s. xi/xii or xii in.
331	Faustina A.x, fols. 3-101	Ælfric, *Grammar*$^+$* and *Glossary*$^+$* ; Maxims$^+$* (s. xi ex.) ; Dialogue on declinations : s. xi^2 or $xi^{3/4}$.
332	Faustina B.iii, fols. 158-198	[with Tiberius A.iii, fols. 174-177] List of Roman emperors (s. xi/xii or xii^1) ; *Regularis Concordia*, c.xiv-xix* ; *Regularis Concordia* ; Three formula-letters announcing the death of a monk : s. xi med., Canterbury CC.

—	Faustina B.vi, fols. 95 and 98-100	[see no. **362**]

333 Galba A.xiv

Prayerbook : Computus tables ; Prayers$^{(*)}$; Three hymns (including SK 685, 1013) ; Apocryphal letter of Christ to Abgar ; Charm* ; Seven psalter collects ; Mass collects and other liturgical pieces ; Two litanies ; 'Celtic capitella' ; Medical recipes* ; Canticle (Benedicite) ; Athanasian Creed : s. xi$^{2/4}$, Winchester?, prov. Winchester Nun or Shaftesbury? [one vol. with Nero A.ii, fols. 3-13?].
FC : *A Pre-Conquest English Prayer-Book*, ed. B. J. Muir, HBS 103 (1988).

334 Galba A.xviii

[with Oxford, Bodleian Library, Rawlinson B.484, fol. 85]
Psalterium Gallicanum ; Canticles : s. ix^1, NE France (Liège area or Rheims area?).
Additions : Prayers : s. ix^2, France ; Metrical calendar ; Computus material : s. x in., England ; Psalter collects ; Litany, Pater noster, Creed and Sanctus, all in Greek : s. x$^{2/4}$, England.
MS in Italy s. ix^2? In England from s. ix^2 or x in., prov. royal court or a Winchester minster.

336 Julius A.ii,
fols. 10-135

Ælfric, *Grammar*$^+$* and *Glossary*$^+$* ; Treatise on Latin verbs : s. xi med.

337 Julius A.vi

Metrical calendar ; Computus material : s. xi in. ; Expositio Hymnorum° ; Monastic canticles° : s. xi^1 or xi med. ; Latin hymn by Peter Damian (AH 48.52) and Latin poem on the liberal arts (SK 188) added s. xi ex. ; all parts prob. Canterbury CC, (prov. Durham).
FC : Gneuss (1968) ; Korhammer (1976).

338 Julius A.x,
fols. 44-175

Old English Martyrology* (incomplete) : s. x/xi.

339 Julius E.vii

Ælfric, Lives of Saints* ; Four anonymous Lives of Saints* ; Ælfric, (version of Alcuin's) *Interrogationes Sigewulfi in Genesin**, *De falsis diis** (f) : s. xi in., S England, (prov. Bury St. Edmunds).

340 Nero A.i,
fols. 3-57

Laws* : *Cnut I, II* ; *Eadgar II, III* ; *Alfred* and *Ine*, Capitula and Introduction ; *Romscot* ; '*Judex*' (from Alcuin, *De virtutibus et vitiis*, c. 20) : s. xi$^{3/4}$.
FC : Loyn (1971).

341 Nero A.i,
fols. 70-177

(A version of Wulfstan's 'Handbook') : Wulfstan, *Institutes of Polity**, four Homilies* ; Laws* : *Æthelstan I, Eadmund I, Eadgar III, Æthelred V, VIII* ; *Grið** ; Texts related to ecclesiastical institutes$^{(*)}$; Wulfstan's Canon Law Collection ('*Excerptiones Pseudo-Egberti*', recension B) ; Abbo of Saint-Germain, two abbrev. sermons :

1003×1023, Worcester or York.
FC : Loyn (1971).

342 Nero A.ii, Calendar ; Computus table ; Poem on King Æthelstan (SK 2143) ;
fols. 3-13 Two prayers ; Latin poem : s. xi$^{2/4}$, Winchester? [part of Galba
A.xiv?].

342.2 Nero A.vii, Lanfranc, *Epistolae* ; Memorandum on the primacy of Canterbury ;
fols. 1-39, Councils of Winchester (1072) and London (1074×75) ; Anselm,
41-112. *Epistolae* (incomplete) : s. xi/xii, England or Normandy, (prov. prob.
Rochester).

342.3 Nero A.vii, Lanfranc's Epitaph ; Recipe for making red and blue dye (f) : s. xi/xii.
fol. 40

342.6 Nero C.v, Marianus Scotus, *Chronicon* : s. xi ex. (after 1086), Continent, with
fols. 1-161 additions s. xi ex. in England, prov. Hereford Cathedral.

342.8 Nero C.ix, [with London, Lambeth Palace 430, flyleaves]
fols. 19-21 Necrology (f ; Aug.-Dec.) : s. xi/xii (prob. in or after 1093),
Canterbury CC.

343 Nero D.iv Gospels° : 687×689, Lindisfarne, prov. Chester-le-Street s. ix ex.,
Durham s. x ex., OE gloss s. x$^{3/4}$, prob. before 970.

344 Nero E.i, Vol. i, fols. 3-54 (additions) : Byrhtferth, *Vitae S. Oswaldi*,
vol.i and vol.ii, *S. Ecgwini* ; Lantfred, *Translatio et miracula S. Swithuni* and hymn by
fols. 1-155 Wulfstan of Winchester (SK 1443) : s. xi$^{3/4}$;
Vol. i, fols. 55-208 and vol. ii, fols. 1-155 : Office legendary (January-
September) ; Office and Mass for St. Nicholas : s. xi$^{3/4}$; whole MS
Worcester [for vol.ii, fols. 166-180 and Companion volume see
no. **36** ; vol. ii, fols. 156-165 are s. xii additions].
FC : Jackson and Lapidge (1996).

344.5 Nero E.i, vol. ii, [with London, B.L. Add. 46204]
fols. 181-184 Cartulary (f) : s. xi ex., Worcester [since s. xi part of no. **293**?].

345 Nero E.i, vol. ii Laws : *Eadgar IV** : s. x/xi ; Office lections (f) : s. xi^1 or xi med. or
fols. 185-186 xi^2, all prov. Worcester?

346 Otho A.i [with Oxford, Bodleian Library Arch. Selden B.26]
Decrees of the Council of Clofesho 747 (f) ; Bonifatius, *Epistola* 78
to Archbishop Cuthbert (f) ; Charter (f) ; Gregory, *Regula pastoralis*,
abridged (f) : s. viii^2, Mercia or Canterbury?

347 Otho A.vi, Boethius (Alfred), *De consolatione Philosophiae** : s. x med.,
fols. 1-129 SE England.

348	Otho A.viii	[with Otho B.x, fol. 66]
		Goscelin, *Vita et Translatio S. Mildrethae* (f) : s. $xi^{4/4}$, Canterbury
		StA? ; Life of St. Machutus* (incomplete, damaged), s. $xi^{1/4}$.

| 349 | Otho A.x | [with Otho A.xii, fols. 1-7] |
| | | Æthelweard, *Chronicon* : s. xi in. |

| — | Otho A.xii, fols. 1-7 | [see no. 349] |

| 350 | Otho A.xii, fols. 8-12, 14-16, 18-19 | Osbern, *Vita et translatio S. Ælphegi* (f) : s. $xi^{3/4}$ or xi^2. |

| 351 | Otho A.xiii pt. i | Fragments from a collection of Saints' lives and visions, including *Vita S. Fursei* ; *Visio Baronti* (*BHL* 997) ; *Visio Wettini* by Heito : s. xi^1 or xi in. |

| 352 | Otho A.xviii, fol. 131 | Ælfric, Homily on St. Laurentius* (f) : s. xi^1. |

| 353 | Otho B.ii | [with Otho B.x, fols. 61, 63 and 64] |
| | | Gregory (Alfred), *Regula pastoralis** (incomplete) : s. x^2 or x/xi, SE England, possibly London. |

| 354 | Otho B.ix | Hymn or prayer (s. x, added in England) ; Gospels (f) ; Inscription* and manumissions* (s. x or xi, all lost) : s. ix^2 or $ix^{4/4}$, Brittany, prov. English royal court s. x^1, Chester-le-Street prob. 934, Durham s. x ex. |

| 355 | Otho B.x (except the fols. of nos. **356** seqq.) | [with Oxford, Bodleian Library, Rawlinson Q.e.20] |
| | | Ælfric, *Hexameron* *; Lives of Saints* and Homilies* (most by Ælfric ; incomplete, damaged) : s. xi^1. |

| 356 | Otho B.x, fols. 29 and 30 | Homilies* (f) : s. xi med., (prov. Worcester). |

| — | Otho B.x, fol. 51 | [see no. **358**] |

| — | Otho B.x, fols. 55, 58 and 62 | [see no. **357**] |

| — | Otho B.x, fols. 61, 63 and 64 | [see no. **353**] |

| — | Otho B.x, fol. 66 | [see no. **348**] |

357   Otho B.xi   [with Otho B.x, fols. 55, 58 and 62, and London, B.L. Add. 34652, fol. 2]
Beda, *Historia ecclesiastica**(f) : s. x med. and (Bede's autobiographical note) s. xi¹ ; West-Saxon royal genealogy* ; *Anglo-Saxon Chronicle* G*(f) ; Laws* : *Æthelstan II* (f), *Alfred* and *Ine* (f) : s. xi¹ ; all parts Winchester, (prov. Southwick, Augustinian canons) [other texts lost].

358   Otho C.i,   [with Otho B.x, fol. 51]
         vol.i   Gospels* (incomplete) : s. xi¹ ; Bull of Pope Sergius* : s. xi med., all prov. Malmesbury?

359   Otho C.i,   Gregory (Werferth), *Dialogi** (incomplete) ; Three lives from *Vitas*
         vol. ii   *Patrum** (From bk.V : *Verba seniorum* v, 37 and 38 ; *Vita S. Malchi* by Jerome) ; Letter of Bonifatius to Eadburg⁺* (*Epist*.10) ; Sermon ('Evil tongues')* ; Three homilies* by Ælfric : s. xi in., SW England? From fol. 62 (*Dialogi*, bk.iii) : s. xi med., prob. Worcester, (prov. whole MS Worcester).

—   Otho C.v   [see no. **63**]

360   Otho E.i   Glossary⁺* : s. x/xi, prob. Canterbury StA, prov. Canterbury CC?

361   Otho E.xiii   *Liber ex lege Moysi* ; *Collectio canonum Hibernensis* (recension A) ; St. Patrick, *Epistola ad episcopos* ; *Canones Wallici* ; *Canones Adamnani* ; Supplement from *Collectio canonum Hibernensis* (recension B) ; Legend of the Seven Sleepers : s. ix/x or x in., Brittany, (prov. Canterbury StA).

362   Tiberius A.ii   [with Claudius A.iii, fols. 2-7 and 9* and Faustina B.vi, vol.i, fols. 95 and 98-100]
Gospels, Gospel list ; Dedication poem praising King Æthelstan (SK 14294) and prose dedication (929×939) ; Records⁽*⁾ (s. xi¹ - xii in.) : s. ix/x or x in., Lobbes, prov. England (royal court) before 939, prov. Canterbury CC s. x¹.

363   Tiberius A.iii,   *Regula S. Benedicti*° ; Ambrosius Autpertus (Pseudo-Fulgentius),
         fols. 2-173   Admonition° ; *Memoriale qualiter*, chs. 10-19° ; '*De festivitatibus anni*' (*Ansegisi Capitularium Collectio* ii.33) ; *Capitulare monasticum* ; *Regularis Concordia*° ; *Somniale Danielis*° ; Prognostics° ; Prognostics⁽*⁾ ; Notes on Adam*, Noah and Old Testament figures*, on the Ages of the World, on Friday fasts*, on the age of the Virgin* ; Prayers⁽*⁾; Handbook for a confessor* ; Office of All Saints (Vespers, Lauds) ; Ælfric, *Colloquy*° ; Ælfric, *De temporibus anni** (part) ; Notes on the dimensions of Noah's Ark, St. Peter's in Rome, the Temple of Solomon ; The names of the thieves hanged with Christ ; Life of St. Margaret* ; Ælfric, *Catholic Homily* II.xiv* ; Sunday letter* ; Devil's account of the next world* ;

Homiletic pieces* ; Examination of a bishop (from pontifical) ; Treatise on monastic sign language* ; Lapidary* ; Excerpt from Isidore, *Synonyma* (sect. 88-96)* ; *Regula S. Benedicti*, ch. iv˙* ; Alcuin, *De virtutibus et vitiis*, chs.14 and 26* ; Charm* ; Ælfric, Pastoral Letter III* ; Office of the Virgin : s. xi med., Canterbury CC.

—	Tiberius A.iii, fols. 174-177	[see no. **332**]
—	Tiberius A.iii, fol. 178	[see no. **364**]
363.2	Tiberius A.iii, fol. 179	Horologium* ; Mass prayer : s. x ex.
364	Tiberius A.vi, fols. 1-35	[with Tiberius A.iii, fol. 178] *Anglo-Saxon Chronicle* B* ; Genealogy of West-Saxon kings* ; Note on finding a piece of the Cross (s. xi/xii) ; List of archbishops of Canterbury and popes (s. xi/xii) : s. x$^{3/4}$, prob. 977×979, prob. Abingdon, prov. Canterbury (prob. CC) s. xi^2.
365	Tiberius A.vii, fols. 165-166	Prosper, *Epigrammata*° (f) and *Versus ad coniugem*° (f) : s. ix$^{3/4}$, W France ; OE gloss s. xi^1.
366	Tiberius A.xiii	Two cartularies ; Homily* (s. xi^1) : c.1016 and c.1096, Worcester.
367	Tiberius A.xiv	Beda, *Historia ecclesiastica* : s. viii med., Wearmouth-J.
368	Tiberius A.xv, fols. 1-173	Alcuin, A selection of his letters ; A collection of letters mainly to tenth-century archbishops of Canterbury : s. xi in., prob. Canterbury CC.
368.2	Tiberius A.xv, fol. 174	Gospel of St. John (conclusion) : s. x ; Charter : s. xi.
369	Tiberius A.xv, fols. 175-180	Junilius, *De partibus divinae legis* (f) : s. vii/viii, prob. S England, (prov. Malmesbury?).
370	Tiberius B.i, fols. 3-111	Orosius, *Historiae adversus paganos** : s. xi^1, prov. prob. Abingdon.
370.2	Tiberius B.i, fols. 112-164	Metrical calendar ('*Menologium*')* ; Gnomic verses ('*Maxims II*')* ; *Anglo-Saxon Chronicle* C* : s. xi med., Abingdon.
371	Tiberius B.ii, fols. 2-85	Abbo of Fleury, *Vita S. Eadmundi* ; Hermannus Archidiaconus, (attrib.)*Miracula S. Eadmundi* (long version, incomplete) : s. xi/xii, (prov. Bury St. Edmunds).

| 372 | Tiberius B.iv, fols. 3-9 and 19-86 | *Anglo-Saxon Chronicle* D* : s. xi med., xi^2, W Midlands (Worcester?), (prov. Worcester, previously Canterbury CC?). |

| — | Tiberius B.iv, fol. 87 | [see no. **521**] |

| 373 | Tiberius B.v, fols. 2-73 and 77-88 | Computus material ('Leofric-Tiberius Computus') ; Metrical calendar ; Beda, *De temporibus* ch.xiv ; Lists of : popes, the seventy-two disciples of Christ (erased), Roman emperors, high priests of Jerusalem, bishops of Jerusalem, Alexandria and Antiochia, 19 lists of bishops of Anglo-Saxon dioceses ; Royal genealogies of Anglo-Saxon kingdoms$^{(*)}$ in 16 lists ; List of the abbots of Glastonbury ; Archbishop Sigeric's journey to Rome ; Ælfric, *De temporibus anni** ; Astronomical texts ; Cicero, *Aratea* with scholia ; Excerpts from : Pliny (*Naturalis historia*), Macrobius (*In Somnium Scipionis*), Martianus Capella ; Map of the world ; Priscian, *Periegesis* ; *Vita, Miracula, Translatio S. Nicolai* (in verse ; SK 7869) ; *Marvels of the East*⁺* ; *Mambres and Jannes*⁺* : s. xi$^{2/4}$, Canterbury CC? Winchester?, (prov. Battle). |

FC : *An Eleventh-Century Anglo-Saxon Illustrated Miscellany*, ed. P. McGurk et al., EEMF 17 (Copenhagen, 1983).

| — | Tiberius B.v, fols. 74 and 76 | [see no. **21**] |

| 374 | Tiberius B.v, fol. 75 | Gospels (f) ; Records* (s. x^1, x med., xi^1) : s. viii, prob. Northumbria, prov. Exeter by s. x^1. |

| 375 | Tiberius B.xi | [with Kassel, Gesamthochschulbibliothek 4°Ms. theol. 131] Gregory (Alfred), *Regula pastoralis** (Tiberius almost completely destroyed) : 890×897, Winchester? |

| 376 | Tiberius C.i, fols. 43-203 | Pontifical (Pontificale Romano-Germanicum) : s. xi^1 or xi med., Germany. Pontifical services, three homilies*, prayers*, four homilies ; Council of Winchester (1070) ; Penitential articles issued after the Battle of Hastings ; Litany : added England 1070×1100, prov. whole MS Sherborne s. xi^2, then (prob. from c. 1075) Salisbury. |

| 377 | Tiberius C.ii | Beda, *Historia ecclesiastica* (with interlinear OE glosses, s. x) ; Glossaries⁺* (s. ix) : s. ix$^{2/4}$, S England, prob. Canterbury (StA?). |

| 378 | Tiberius C.vi | Computus material ('Winchester Computus', fragmentary) ; Picture cycle ; Notes on *Psalterium, Alleluia, Gloria* ; Prayers ; Ordo confessionis with litany ; Homily⁺* ; Psalterium Gallicanum° (now incomplete) with psalter collects : s. xi$^{3/4}$, prob. mid 1060s, Winchester OM? |

378.5	Tiberius D.iv, fols. 1-105	42 Lives of Saints (including 'Martinellus') : s. xi/xii, N France (or England?), prov. prob. Winchester OM. FC : Th. Smith, *Catalogue of the Manuscripts in the Cottonian Library 1696*, repr. and ed. C. G. C. Tite (Cambridge, 1984), pp. 27-28.
—	Tiberius D.iv fols. 158-166	[see no. **759**]
379	Titus A.iv	*Regula S. Benedicti*[+]* ; Capitulare monasticum ; *Memoriale qualiter* ; '*De festivitatibus anni*' (*Ansegisi Capitularium collectio* ii.33) : s. xi med., Winchester? Canterbury StA?
379.5	Titus D.xvi, fols. 2-35	Prudentius, *Psychomachia* ; Poem on St. Laurentius : s. xi/xii, St. Albans.
380	Titus D.xxvi and xxvii	Lunaria ; Prognostics ; Calendar with necrology ; Computus material ('Winchester Computus'); Ælfric, *De temporibus anni** ; Alphabet with OE sentences* ; The Passion according to St. John chs. xviii-xix ; Devotions to the Holy Cross ; Offices of the Trinity, the Holy Cross, the Virgin ; Private prayers ; Directions for private devotions* ; Note in cryptography ; Notes on the names of the Seven Sleepers, on the age of the Virgin*, the Ages of the World, the length of Christ's body, on the rainbow ; *Somniale Danielis* ; Medical recipe* ; Rules of confraternity* ; Collectar ; Litany ; Gospel of St. John i.1-14 : 1023×1031, Winchester NM.
381	Vespasian A.i	Introductory texts to the psalms (including SK 10728, 12730) ; Interpretations of *Alleluia*, *Gloria* and Hebrew letters (in Psalm 118) ; Psalterium Romanum° ; Canticles° ; Three hymns° (SK 15627, 3544, 14234) : s. viii[2/4], prob. Canterbury StA, OE gloss s. ix (prob. s. ix med.) ; *Te Deum*° ; *Quicumque vult*° ; Prayers : s. xi[1], Canterbury (CC?), (prov. whole MS Canterbury StA).
382	Vespasian A.viii, fols. 1-33	Latin distich ; New Minster Charter : 966, Winchester OM, prov. Winchester NM.
383	Vespasian A.xiv, fols. 114-179	(Letter-book of Archbishop Wulfstan) : Alcuin, A selection of his letters ; Various letters, mainly by popes, and to tenth-century Anglo-Saxon bishops ; Poem addressed to Archbishop Wulfstan (SK 13280) ; Decrees of the Councils of Chelsea (816) and Hertford (672) ; Constitutiones of Archbishop Oda (942×946) : 1003×1023, Worcester or York.
384	Vespasian B.vi, fols. 1-103	Beda, *De temporum ratione* ; Lists of Carolingian rulers and Byzantine emperors : s. ix[2/4], Saint-Denis, prov. England by s. xi in.

385	Vespasian B.vi, fols. 104-109	'Metrical calendar of York' ; Notes on the Ages of the World, on the Ages of Man, on the human body, on the dimensions of the world, of the Temple of Solomon, of the Tabernacle, of St. Peter's in Rome, of Noah's Ark, on the books of the Bible, on measures of length ; Lists of popes, the seventy disciples of Christ, Anglo-Saxon bishops ; Anglian royal genealogies : 805×814, Mercia.
386	Vespasian B.x, fols. 31-124	Aethicus Ister, *Cosmographia* : s. x/xi, prob. Worcester, (prov. ibid.).
387	Vespasian B.xx	Goscelin, *Vitae* and *Miracula S. Augustini* [of Canterbury] (*Historia minor* and *maior*) ; Goscelin, *Translatio S. Augustini, Vita S. Letardi, Vita* and *Translatio S. Mildrethae, Vitae* of the early archbishops of Canterbury (Laurentius, Mellitus, Justus, Honorius, Deusdedit, Theodore) and of Abbot Hadrian ; Gregory and Augustine, *Libellus responsionum* ; Goscelin(?), *Libellus contra usurpatores S. Mildrethae* ; Royal and papal privileges for St. Augustine's Abbey : s. xi/xii, Canterbury StA.
388	Vespasian D.ii	Penitential texts ; Adso, *De Antichristo* ; Canons ; Homilies (including Wulfstan Ia) and saints' miracles ; Decreta pontificum : s. xi/xii, Normandy, in England by 1100?
389	Vespasian D.vi, fols. 2-77	Proverbia Salomonis° ; Glosses on Proverbia Salomonis ; Alcuin, *De virtutibus et vitiis*° ; Macarius, from *Verba seniorum* xviii.9 (*Vitas Patrum*, bk.V) ; Kentish Hymn* ; Note on the Ages of the World* ; Kentish Psalm* ; *Disticha Catonis* (incomplete) ; Texts from Mass of the Virgin ; Verse antiphon for St. Augustine of Canterbury ; Dialogue before the Cross (s. xi/xii) ; Latin terms of relationship° : s. x med. (or x²), prob. Canterbury StA, (prov. ibid.).
390	Vespasian D.vi, fols. 78-125	Stephen of Ripon, *Vita S. Wilfridi* : s. xi$^{4/4}$ (s. xi ex. or later?), Northumbria?, (prov. Yorkshire).
391	Vespasian D.xii	Introductory note (from Isidore) and poem ; Hymnal ; Expositio hymnorum° ; Monastic canticles° : s. xi med., Canterbury CC. FC : Gneuss (1968) ; Korhammer (1976).
392	Vespasian D.xiv, fols. 170-224	Isidore, *Synonyma* ; Four Creeds (attrib. to Ambrose, Gregory, Jerome) ; Hymns (SK 12515 (f), 10768) : s. ix$^{1/4}$, N or NE France, prov. s. x in. (before 912) S England ; Additions : Excerpts from Boethius, *De consolatione Philosophiae* : i. metr. 1 and 2, iii. metr. 8, iv. metr. 7 ; Note on dating the *annus praesens* : s. x in., England, (whole MS prov. Canterbury CC?).
393	Vespasian D.xv, fols. 68-101	Collections concerning confession and penance ; *Poenitentiale Theodori* : s. x med.

394	Vespasian D.xv, fols. 102-121	Excerpts from Amalarius, *Liber officialis* (Retractatio prima) ; Exegesis and rhyming version of Pater noster ; Duties of a priest : s. x/xi, W England (Worcester?).
395	Vespasian D.xx fols. 2-86	Manual of confessional and penitential texts : s. x med.
395.5	Vespasian D.xx, fols. 87-93	Confessional prayer* : s. x^1 (c. 910×c. 930) ; Charm against toothache : s. xi^2.
—	Vespasian D.xxi, fols. 18-40	[see no. **657**]
396	Vitellius A.vi	Gildas, *De excidio Britanniae* (incomplete) : s. x med., prob. Canterbury StA.
397	Vitellius A.vii, fols. 1-112	Pontifical (incomplete), including two abbrev. sermons by Abbo of Saint-Germain : prob. Ramsey after 1030, and Exeter, 1046×1072.
398	Vitellius A.xii, fols. 4-77	*Dialogus Egberti* ; Abbo of Fleury, *De differentia circuli et sphaerae* (pt. ii : '*De cursu septem planetarum*') ; Hrabanus Maurus, *De computo* ; Miscellaneous short texts, and poems (as in no. **258**) mainly computistical ; Isidore, *De natura rerum* ; Abbo of Fleury, *De duplici signorum ortu vel occasu* ; Greek, Hebrew and runic alphabets ; Calendar : s. xi ex., Salisbury.
399	Vitellius A.xv, fols. 94-209	Homily on St. Christopher* ; *Marvels of the East** ; *Letter of Alexander to Aristotle** ; *Beowulf** ; *Judith** (incomplete) : s. x/xi.
400	Vitellius A.xviii	Computus tables ; Calendar ; Prayers ; Sacramentary ; Benedictional ; Penitential texts ; Selection of pontifical services : s. xi^2, prov. SW England (Wells?).
401	Vitellius A.xix	Beda, *Vitae S. Cuthberti* (prose and verse) ; Excerpts from Beda, *Historia ecclesiastica* ; Four Latin poems (incl. SK 15347, from Juvencus i.589-603, and *De quattuor clavibus sapientiae*, as in no. **903**) and note on the Ages of Man (s. x^2) : s. $x^{2/4}$ or x med., prob. Canterbury StA, prov. prob. ibid. s. x/xi.
402	Vitellius C.iii, fols. 11-85	Enlarged *Herbarius** (Antonius Musa, *De herba vettonica* ; Pseudo-Apuleius, *Herbarius* ; Herbs from Pseudo-Dioscorides, *Liber medicinae ex herbis femininis* and *Curae herbarum*) ; *Medicina de quadrupedibus** (*De taxone liber* ; Treatise on mulberry tree ; Sextus Placitus, *Liber medicinae ex animalibus*) ; Medical recipes$^{(*)}$ (s. xi med. - xi/xii) : s. xi^1 or xi med., Canterbury CC?
402.5	Vitellius C.iii, fols. 86-138	Macrobius, *Saturnalia* (bks. i and ii only) : s. $ix^{3/4}$, N France, prov. England before 1100?

403	Vitellius C.v	Ælfric, *Catholic Homilies* (First Series, considerably expanded)* : s. x/xi, and additions s. xi^1, SW England, (prov. Tavistock?).
404	Vitellius C.viii, fols. 22-25	*Dies Aegyptiaci** ; Ælfric, *De temporibus anni** (f) ; Computus notes* : s. xi^1.
—	Vitellius C.viii, fols. 85-90	[see no. **173**]
405	Vitellius C.xii, fols. 114-156	Martyrologium (Usuard) with obits ; Confraternity notes : s. xi ex., or s. xii in.? Canterbury StA.
406	Vitellius D.xvii, fols. 4-92	Ælfric, originally 45 items from *Catholic Homilies** and Lives of Saints* (many now lost or fragmentary) ; *Passio S. Pantaleonis** : s. xi med.
406.5	Vitellius E.xii, fols. 116-160	fols. 116-152 : Pontifical (Pontificale Romano-Germanicum) : s. xi^1, Germany, prob. Cologne, prov. York s. xi^2. fols. 153-60 : Additions : Benedictions ; Hymn (SK 5629) ; parts of Office of the Dead with sermon ; *Laudes regiae* : s. xi^2 (after 1068), Exeter, prov. whole MS Exeter. FC : M. Lapidge, *Anglo-Latin Literature 900-1066* (London, 1993), pp. 466-467 and 454-457.
407	Vitellius E.xviii	Calendar ; Computus material$^{(*)}$ ('Winchester Computus', fragmentary) ; Prognostics* ; Charms* ; Two veterinary recipes* ; Prayers ; Explanations of secret writing^{+*} ; Psalterium Gallicanum° with 'argumenta' ; Canticles° (incomplete) : s. xi med. or xi$^{3/4}$, Winchester NM, (prov. Winchester OM).

– Egerton

408	267, fol. 37	Boethius, *De consolatione Philosophiae* (f), with gloss : s. x ex., prob. Abingdon.
409	874	Caesarius of Arles, *In Apocalypsin* : s. ix^2, NE France ; Additions : Two Easter hymns (SK 2153, 16087), prayers, part of Office of St. Augustine of Canterbury : s. xi^2, England, (prov. all Canterbury StA).
410	1046	Bible or Old Testament (part) : Proverbia (incomplete), Ecclesiastes, Canticum canticorum, Sapientia, Ecclesiasticus (incomplete) : s. viii, Northumbria.
410.5	3278	Beda, *Historia ecclesiastica* (f) : s. xi in.

411	3314, fols. 9-72	[with London, B.L., Cotton Caligula A. xv, fols. 120-153] Calig. 120-141, Eg. 9-44, Calig. 142-3 : Computus material(*) ('Canterbury Computus') ; Prognostics* ; Charms(*) ; Annals of Christ Church, Canterbury+* (with later additions, Calig. 136-139) ; Notes* on Friday fasts, the Ages of the World, the age of the Virgin, on Christ, Adam and Noah ; Pseudo-Damasus and Pseudo-Jerome, Colloquy on celebrating Mass* ; Hermannus Contractus, *Computus*, chs. 1-25 ; List of the archbishops of Canterbury (add. s. xi/xii) ; Extracts from Ælfric, *De temporibus anni**, chs. VI-VIII : s. xi ex. (in and after 1073). Calig. 144-153 : Ælfric, *De temporibus anni**, chs. IV-XI.4 : s. xi/xii. Eg. 45-72 : Computus material : s. xi/xii. All parts Canterbury CC (and StA?).

– Harley

411.6	12, fols. 1-140	Johannes Diaconus, *Vita S. Gregorii* : s. xi ex., prov. Durham?, (prov. Winchester?).
411.7	12, fols. 141-143	*Vita S. Katherinae* : s. xi ex. or xi/xii, prob. England.
412	55, fols. 1-4	Medical recipes* ; Laws* : *Eadgar II, III* ; Record* : s. xi¹, prob. York, or Worcester?, (prov. Worcester).
413	76	Gospels, Gospel list ; Documents (s. xi ex.) : s. xi¹, prob. Canterbury CC, prov. s. xi ex. Bury St. Edmunds.
414	107	Ælfric, *Grammar+** and *Glossary+** ; Dialogue on declinations ; Glossary+* : s. xi med., SE England.
415	110	Prosper, *Epigrammata* and *Versus ad coniugem* ; Isidore, *Synonyma* ; all glossed : s. x ex., Canterbury CC.
416	110, fols. 1 and 56	Gradual (f) : s. xi med., Winchester OM?
417	208	Alcuin, A selection of his letters and three poems (*carm.* 48, 45, 40) ; Dungal, seven Letters ; Letter from Charlemagne to Michael Paleologus : s. ix¹, Saint-Denis, prov. England s. x/xi, (prov. York).
418	213	Alcuin, *In Ecclesiasten* and *In Canticum canticorum* ; Two homilies : s. ix³ᐟ³, France, (prov. Winchester OM, by s. xvi York).
418.3	271, fols. 1* and 45*	Missal (f) : s. xi² or xi ex.
418.8	521, fol. 2	Beda, *De schematibus et tropis* (f) : s. x/xi.

419	526, fols. 1-27	Beda, *Vita S. Cuthberti* (verse) : s. ix ex., NE France, prov. England by s. x med.
421	585	Enlarged *Herbarius**, part (Pseudo-Apuleius, *Herbarius* ; Herbs from Pseudo-Dioscorides, *Liber medicinae ex herbis femininis* and *Curae herbarum*) ; *Medicina de quadrupedibus** (*De taxone liber* ; Treatise on mulberry tree ; part of Sextus Placitus, *Liber medicinae ex animalibus*) ; *Lacnunga** (medical recipes, prayers, charms ; some in Latin and Irish), including *Lorica* of Laidcenn° (SK 15745) and *Dies Ægyptiaci** : s. x/xi and s. xi^1. FC : *ASM* 1, pp. 28-35.
422	603	Psalterium Romanum (Ps 100-105,25 : Gallicanum) : s. x/xi or xi^1, Canterbury CC.
423	647	Prayer ; Astronomical compilation, including : *De nominibus stellarum* (add. England s. x/xi) ; Cicero, *Aratea*, with explanatory excerpts from Hyginus, *Astronomica* ; Excerpts from Macrobius (*In Somnium Scipionis*), Martianus Capella, Pliny (*Naturalis historia*) s. ix$^{2/4}$ (c. 830), Lotharingia, prov. Fleury?, prov. England (Ramsey?) s. x/xi, (prov. Canterbury StA). FC : Saxl and Meier (1953), pp. 149-151.
423.3	648, fol. 207	Missal (f) : s. xi, Continent?
423.9	652, fols. 1*-4*	Alanus of Farfa, *Homiliarium* (f) : s. ix med., prob. N France, (prov. Canterbury StA).
424	652	Paulus Diaconus, *Homiliarium* ; Goscelin, *Vitae* (all abridged and in lessons) of St. Mildred, Abbot Hadrian and four early archbishops of Canterbury (Laurentius, Justus, Honorius, Theodore) : s. xi/xii, Canterbury StA. FC : Richards (1988), pp. 104-108.
424.5	683, fol. 1	Office book (f) : s. xi, England?
425	863, fols. 8-125	Psalterium Gallicanum (with some antiphons) ; Canticles (*Quicumque vult°*) ; Litany ; Prayers ; Offices ; Office of the Dead (part) : 1046×1072, Exeter. FC : Dewick and Frere (1914-21), i.445-54.
426	865	Ambrose, *De mysteriis, De sacramentis* ; Eusebius Gallicanus, *Sermo* 17 ; Jerome, *Contra Jovinianum* ; Pseudo-Augustine, *Hypomnesticon* : s. xi ex., (prov. St. Albans).
427	1117	Verses on the Translation of St. Edward King and Martyr ; Beda, *Vita S. Cuthberti* (prose) ; Excerpts from Beda, *Historia ecclesiastica*

(IV.xxix-xxx) ; Office of St. Cuthbert ; Beda, *Vita S. Cuthberti* (verse) ; Offices of St. Benedict and St. Guthlac : s. x/xi, prob. Canterbury CC.

428	2110, fols. 4* and 5*	Ælfric, *Catholic Homilies** (f : from I.iii-iv) : s. xi^1, (prov. Castle Acre, Norfolk, Cluniac priory?).

428.4   2506   Two prayers (one in verse : SK 7896) ; Hyginus, *Astronomica* ; Pseudo-Priscian, *Carmen de sideribus* (SK 151) ; Abbo of Fleury, *De differentia circuli et sphaerae* ; A collection of texts dealing with astronomy, including : *De nominibus stellarum* ; Cicero, *Aratea*, with scholia ; Excerpts from Pliny (*Naturalis historia*), Macrobius (*In Somnium Scipionis*), Martianus Capella ; *Preceptum canonis Ptolemaei* (Latin version, incomplete) ; Martianus Capella, *De nuptiis Philologiae et Mercurii*, bk.viii (incomplete) ; Remigius, Commentary on Martianus Capella, bk.viii (incomplete) : s. x/xi, Fleury, prov. England s. xi^1.
FC : Saxl and Meier (1953), pp. 157-160.

428.5   2729   Frontinus, *Strategemata* ; Eutropius, *Breviarium historiae Romanae* : s. xi ex., Durham.

429   2892   Benedictional : s. xi$^{2/4}$, Canterbury CC (or Winchester, for use at Canterbury?).
FC : *The Canterbury Benedictional*, ed. R. M. Woolley, HBS 51 (1917).

430   2904   Psalterium Gallicanum ; Canticles ; Litany : s. x$^{3/3}$ or x ex., Winchester? (for Ramsey?), or Ramsey?

431   2961   Collectar ; Hymnal ; Sequences : s. xi$^{3/4}$, Exeter.
FC : Dewick and Frere (1914-21).

432   2965   Prayerbook : Gospel extracts ; Prayers ; *Lorica* of Laidcenn (SK 15745) ; Two charms ; Record* (s. ix/x) ; Forms of confession and absolution, prayer (s. x^1): s. viii/ix or ix^1, Mercia or S England?, prov. Winchester Nun.
FC : *An Ancient Manuscript of the Eighth or Ninth Century*, ed. W. de Gray Birch (London, 1889), pp. 39-97; *ASM* 1, pp. 38-43.

433   3020, fols. 1-34   Beda, Homily on Benedict Biscop (*Homiliae in Evangelia*, I.13) ; Beda, *Historia abbatum* ; Anon., *Vita Ceolfridi* (*BHL* 1726) : s. x/xi, Glastonbury or Canterbury StA?, (prov. Glastonbury).

433.1   3020, fol. 35   Troper (f) : s. xi in.

433.2	3020, fols. 36-94	Eight Lives of Saints ; Sequence (f ; SK 10021) and Responsory (s. xi[1]) : s. x/xi, Canterbury CC, (prov. Glastonbury). FC : J. P. Carley, *ASE* 23 (1994), 276-277.
433.3	3020, fols. 95-132	Riddle ; *Passio S. Julianae* (*BHL* 4523) ; Eutychianos, *Theophili Actus* (trans. Paulus Diaconus of Naples ; *BHL* 8121) : s. x/xi, Winchester?, (prov. Glastonbury).
434	3080	Augustine, *Confessiones*, with *Retractatio* II.vi : s. xi ex. or xi/xii, W England.
434.5	3097	Jerome, *In Danielem* ; *Vitae S. Nicholai* (by Otloh), *S. Botulphi* (by Folcard), *SS. Tancredi, Torhtredi and Tovae* ; Translatio Sanctorum at Thorney ; Felix, *Vita S. Guthlaci* (incomplete) ; Pseudo-Ambrose, *De dignitate sacerdotali* ('*De observantia episcoporum*') ; Ambrose, *De mysteriis, De sacramentis* ; (anon.?), *De utilitate et laude sancti ieiunii* ; Selections from *Vita* and *Miracula S. Nicolai* : s. xi/xii, (prov. Peterborough).
435	3271	Grammatical notes[*]; *Tribal Hidage** ; Notes on the nations, on the thirty silver coins of Judas*, on Noah's Ark*, on Solomon's gold* ; Ælfric, *Grammar*[+]* ; Prognostics[*] ; Computus notes* ; Latin grammar ; Part of Office for Invention of St. Stephen ; Abbo of Saint-Germain, *Bella Parisiacae urbis*, bk.iii (prose version° and verse) ; Missa pro sacerdote ; Glossary material ; Ælfric, Sermon* and excerpts from Letter to Sigeweard* ; The Ages of the World ('*De initio creaturae*')* ; Sequence incipit (SK 14655, by Notker) : s. xi[1].
436	3376	[with Oxford, Bodleian Library, Lat.misc.a.3, fol. 49 and Lawrence, University of Kansas, Spencer Research Library, Pryce P2A] Glossary[+]* : s. x/xi, W England (Worcester?), (prov. prob. Worcester).
—	3405, fol. 4	[see no. **277**]
438	3826	Alcuin, *De orthographia* ; Beda, *De orthographia* ; Abbo of Saint-Germain, *Bella Parisiacae urbis*, bk.iii, glossed ; Martianus Capella, *De nuptiis Philologiae et Mercurii*, bk.iv ; Glossaries, including Greek-Latin list of grammatical and metrical terms, and glosses to Juvenal : s. x/xi, prob. Abingdon.
439	3859	Vegetius, *Epitome rei militaris* ; Computus notes ; Macrobius, *Saturnalia* ; (Pseudo?-)Sallust and Pseudo-Cicero, *Invectivae* ; 'Nennius', *Historia Brittonum* ; *Annales Cambriae* ; Augustine, *De haeresibus* (f) ; Solinus, *Collectanea* ; *Cantus avium* ; Aethicus Ister, *Cosmographia* ; Vitruvius, *De architectura* : s. xi/xii or xii in., England or France?

439.6	5431, fol. 140	Gregory, *Regula pastoralis* (f) : s. ix, prob. Wales, (prov. Worcester).
440	5431, fols. 4-126	Computus material ; *Regula S. Benedicti* ; *Capitulare monasticum* ; *Memoriale qualiter* ; '*De festivitatibus anni*' (*Ansegisi Capitularium collectio* ii.33 ; f) : s. x/xi or x^2 or $x^{4/4}$, prob. Canterbury StA, (prov. ibid.).
440.5	5915, fol. 2	Augustine, *In Johannis epistolam ad Parthos*, tractatus V (f) : s. xi med.
441	5915, fols. 8 and 9	[with Bloomington, Indiana University, Lilly Library, Add. 1000] Ælfric, *Grammar*$^+$* (f) : s. xi^1.
441.1	5915, fol. 10	[with Weinheim, Sammlung E. Fischer, s.n., lost] Justinus, Epitome of Pompeius Trogus, *Historiae Philippicae* (f) : s. viii med., prob. Northumbria.
441.3	5915, fol. 12	Augustine, *Contra mendacium* (f), *De cura pro mortuis gerenda* (f) : s. xi ex. (1080s), Canterbury CC.
442	5915, fol. 13	[with Cambridge, Magdalene College, Pepys 2981(16)] Ælfric, *Catholic Homilies**(f : from I.xx and xxviii) : s. xi in.
—	5977, no. 59	[see no. **524**]
442.3	5977, no. 62	Gospels (f) : s. x/xi or xi in.
442.4	5977, nos. 64 and 71	Excerpts from Beda, *De arte metrica* (f) and Isidore, *Etymologiae*, bk.I : s. x/xi or xi, Continent? In England before 1100?
443	7653	Prayerbook (fragmentary : eight prayers, including SK 7891) : s. viii/ix or ix in., Mercia (Worcester?). FC : *ASM* 1, pp. 50-51.

– Royal

444	1.A.xviii	Gospels (for use in the Mass) : s. ix/x or x in., Brittany, prov. England (royal court?), prob. Canterbury StA by 924×939, (prov. ibid.).
445	1.B.vii	Gospels ; Manumission* (c.925) : s. viii^1, prob. Northumbria, prov. S England (royal court?) s. x^1.
446	1.D.iii	Gospels : s. xi med., prov. Rochester s. xi ex.

447	1.D.ix	Gospels, Gospel list ; Records* (before 1019) : s. xi in., Canterbury CC (or Peterborough?), prov. s. xi (prob. by 1018) Canterbury CC.
448	1.E.vi	[with Canterbury, Cathedral Library, Add. 16 and Oxford, Bodleian Library, Lat.bib.b.2(P)] Bible (part) : Gospels (incomplete), Actus Apostolorum (f) : s. ix^1 or ix$^{2/4}$ or ix med., S England, (prov. Canterbury StA).
449	1.E.vii and 1.E.viii	Bible : s. x/xi, prov. Canterbury CC.
450	2.A.xx	Prayerbook : Gospel extracts ; Pater noster°, Credo° ; Apocryphal letter of Christ to Abgar ; Three canticles° ; Two charms ; Prayers (including SK 708, 9504) ; Litany ; Two creeds (including SK 9568) ; Note on moonrise* ; Exorcism ; Two hymns (SK 33, by Sedulius ; SK 588) : s. viii^2 or ix$^{1/4}$, Mercia (Worcester?), OE glosses and note s. x^1 ; 33 Prayers (mainly collects from Mass and Office) add. s. x med., Worcester. FC : Kuypers (1902), pp. 201-225 ; Warner and Gilson (1921), I.33-36; *ASM* 1, pp. 53-58.
451	2.B.v	Psalterium Romanum° with commentary ; Canticles° : s. x med., prov. Winchester, prov. Canterbury CC s. xi ; Additions : Notes on Christ's Incarnation, Christ, 'Pascha Christianorum', the Ages of the World (followed by Bede, *De temporibus* ch. xvi), Chronology, the Ages of Man, the human body ; The dimensions of the world, the Temple of Solomon, the Tabernacle, St. Peter's in Rome, Noah's Ark ; on the books of the Bible, on measures of length ; Thunder prognostics ; Prayers* ; Note on Friday fasts* : s. x ex. - xi^1 ; Prayer : s. xi in., Winchester ; Office of the Virgin : s. xi med. or xi^2, Winchester Nun? Proverbs$^+$*, Prayer* : s. xi med.
452	2.C.iii	Paulus Diaconus, *Homiliarium* (Septuagesima to Sabbatum Sanctum, Sanctorale, Commune SS.) : s. xi/xii, (prov. Rochester). FC : Richards (1988), pp. 98-101.
453	2.E.xiii and 2.E.xiv	Pseudo-Jerome, *Breviarium in Psalmos* (Ps 1-100 only) : s. x ex.
453.2	3.B.i	Isidore, *Quaestiones in Vetus Testamentum* ; Jerome, *In Epistolas Pauli ad Titum, ad Philemonem* : s. xi/xii, (prov. Rochester).
453.4	3.B.xvi	Jerome, *In Hieremiam* : s. xi/xii, (prov. Bath).
453.6	3.C.iv	Liber Job ; Gregory, *Moralia*, bks. 1-17 [Companion vol. to no. **469.3**] : s. xi/xii, (prov. Rochester).

453.8	3.C.x	Gospel of St. John ; Augustine, *In Evangelium Johannis* : s. xi/xii, (prov. Rochester).
454	4.A.xiv, fols. 1* and 2*	Missal (f) : s. ix ex., Continent (France? Italy s. ix/x?). In England (Worcester?) from s. ix/x?, (prov. Worcester).
455	4.A.xiv, fols. 1-106	Jerome, *Tractatus in Psalmos* (with interpolations from Pseudo-Jerome, *Breviarium in Psalmos*) ; Excerpts from Origenes (Rufinus), Homilies on Numeri : s. x med., Winchester?, (prov. Worcester).
456	4.A.xiv, fols. 107 and 108	Felix, *Vita S. Guthlaci* (f) : s. viii/ix or ix in. or ix[1], S England (Winchester?) or Mercia, (prov. Worcester).
456.2	5.A.xii, fols. iii-vi	Missal (f) : s. xi med. or xi[2], Worcester.
456.4	5.B.ii	Augustine, *De pastoribus* (*Sermo* 46), *De ovibus* (*Sermo* 47), *De baptismo contra Donatistas, De peccatorum meritis et remissione et de baptismo parvulorum, De unico baptismo contra Petilianum, De spiritu et littera* : s. xi/xii, (prov. Bath).
456.6	5.B.vi	Augustine, *In Johannis Epistolam ad Parthos* ; Quodvultdeus (Pseudo-Augustine), *Sermo contra Arianos, Judaeos et paganos* ; Apocalypsis Johannis ; Canticum canticorum : s. xi/xii, (prov. Rochester).
456.8	5.B.xiv	Augustine : *Confessiones*, with *Retractatio* II.vi : s. xi/xii or xii[1], Gloucester?, (prov. Bath).
457	5.B.xv, fols. 57-64	Johannes Chrysostomus (in Latin), *De muliere Cananaea* ; Goscelin, *Miracula S. Letardi* (in lessons) : s. xi ex., Canterbury StA.
457.4	5.D.i, and 5.D.ii	Augustine, *In Psalmos* (51-100 and 101-150) : s. xi/xii, (prov. Rochester).
457.6	5.E.vii, fol. i	Gradual (f) : s. xi[1].
457.8	5.E.x	Julianus Pomerius, *De vita contemplativa* : s. xi/xii, (prov. Rochester).
458	5.E.xi	Aldhelm, *De virginitate* (prose)° : s. x/xi, OE glosses s. xi in., xi med. ; all Canterbury CC.
459	5.E.xiii	Pseudo-Jerome, *Liber 'Canon in Hebreica'* ; Cyprian, *Ad Quirinum Testimonia*, bk.iii ; Selections from *Collectio canonum Hibernensis* ; (Pseudo-)Beda-Egbert Poenitentiale ('additivum' version) ; Penitential texts ; Excerpt from Book of Enoch (ch.106, abbrev., in Latin) ; *De vindictis magnorum peccatorum* ; Gospel of Nicodemus

(incomplete) : s. ix ex., N France or Brittany, prov. England
by s. x med., (prov. Worcester).

460	5.E.xvi	Pseudo-Augustine, *De unitate S. Trinitatis* (incomplete) ; Excerpts in dialogue form from Isidore, *Differentiae* and *Etymologiae* ; Isidore, *De fide catholica* : s. xi ex., Salisbury.
461	5.E.xix	Isidore, *Synonyma* ; Two homilies ; Twelve homilies from Homiliary of Saint-Père, Chartres ; Alcuin, *In Canticum canticorum* ; Anon. commentary on Canticum canticorum : s. xi ex., Salisbury. FC : Warner and Gilson (1921), I.118 ; Webber (1992), p. 145.
462	5.F.iii	Aldhelm, *De virginitate* (prose) : s. ix ex. or ix/x, Mercia (Worcester?), (prov. Worcester).
463	5.F.xiii	Ambrose, *Epistolae*, *De obitu Theodosii* ; Pseudo-Ambrose, *De Protasio et Gervasio* (*Epist.* 22), Ambrose, *De Nabuthae* : s. xi ex., prov. Salisbury.
463.5	5.F.xviii, fols. 29^v-32	Pseudo-Methodius, *Revelationes* : s. xi ex., Salisbury.
464	6.A.vi	Aldhelm, *Epistola ad Heahfridum*, *De virginitate* (prose)° : s. x ex., Canterbury CC.
464.9	6.A.vii, fols. 1 and 162^v	Responsory ; Prefatory letter to Gregory, *Homiliae in Ezechielem* ; Two Anglo-Saxon alphabets : s. xi ex. and xi/xii, Worcester.
465	6.A.vii	Johannes Diaconus, *Vita S. Gregorii* : s. xi in., Worcester.
466	6.B.vii	Aldhelm, *De virginitate* (prose)° ; List of relics (s. xi/xii) : s. xi ex., (prov. Exeter).
467	6.B.viii, fols. 1-57	Isidore, *De fide catholica*, bk.i ; Alcuin, *Epistolae* 175 and 304, *De fide sanctae et individuae Trinitatis*, *De animae ratione* : s. xi^2, Canterbury StA?
468	6.B.xii, fol. 38	Pontifical (f) : s. xi^2.
469	6.C.i	Isidore, *Etymologiae* : s. xi^{1}or xi^2, Canterbury StA, (prov. ibid.).
469.3	6.C.vi	Gregory, *Moralia*, bks. 17-35 ; Lanfranc's notes on the *Moralia* [Companion vol. to no. **453.6**] : s. xi/xii, (prov. Rochester).
469.5	6.C.x	Gregory (?), *Symbolum fidei* ; Gregory, *Registrum epistolarum* : s. xi/xii, (prov. Rochester).

470	7.C.iv	Defensor of Ligugé, *Liber scintillarum*° ; 'Pauca de vitiis et peccatis'° (extracts from Ecclesiasticus and Isidore, *Sententiae*) : s. xi[1], Canterbury CC?, (prov. ibid.) ; OE gloss s. xi med.
(471)	7.C.xii, fols. 2 and 3	[see now no. **63**]
472	7.C.xii, fols. 4-218	Ælfric, *Catholic Homilies* (First Series)* : s. x ex. (prob. 990), SW England, prob. Cerne.
473	7.D.xxiv, fols. 82-168	Aldhelm, *De virginitate* (prose), with gloss (s. $x^{2/4}$ - x med.) ; *Epistola ad Heahfridum* : s. x[1], S England (Wessex? Glastonbury?).
474	8.B.xi	Paschasius Radbertus, *De corpore et sanguine Domini* ; Unidentified extract : s. x^2, prob. Worcester.
474.5	8.B.xiv, fols. 118-144	(All texts are for feasts of St. Judoc) : Isembard of Fleury, *Inventio corporis* (incomplete), *Miracula* ; Homily ; Lupus of Ferrières, Sermon ; Masses for Invention and Translation, two hymns, (SK 11580, 1319), prayer : s. xi[1], France (Saint-Josse, Brittany?) ; Metrical life of St. Judoc (SK 16714) : s. xi[2], England ; both parts in England (Winchester?) by s. xi ex.
474.6	8.B.xiv, fols. 154-156	Commentary on Canticum canticorum (f) : s. xi ex., Salisbury.
475	8.C.iii	Pseudo-Jerome, *De generibus musicorum* (*Epist.*23) ; *Expositio missae* ('Primum in ordine') ; Theodulf, *De ordine baptismi* ; Commentary on words of baptismal office ; Confession of faith (partly from Gennadius) ; Explanation of terms connected with baptism ; Alcuin, *De sacramento baptismatis* (*Epist.* 134) ; *Expositio missae* ('Dominus vobiscum') ; Augustine, *De magistro* : s. x ex., Canterbury StA.
476	8.C.vii, fols. 1 and 2	Ælfric, Lives of Saints* (f) : s. xi in.
477	8.F.xiv, fols. 3 and 4	Vergil, *Aeneid* (f), with scholia : s. xi in., prob. Continent, (prov. Bury St. Edmunds).
478	12.C.xxiii	Julian of Toledo, *Prognosticon futuri saeculi*, with glosses ; Aldhelm, Symphosius, Eusebius, Tatwine : *Aenigmata* (with glosses and scholia) ; *Opus monitorium* (attributed, erroneously, to Smaragdus) ; Pseudo-Smaragdus, Pseudo-Alcuin, Two monitory poems for a prince (SK 7810, 10988) ; *Versus cuiusdam Scotti de alphabeto* (SK 12594) : s. x^2 or x/xi, Canterbury CC.

478.5	12.D.iv	Calendar (without saints' feasts) ; Computus tables ; Helperic, *De computo* ; Beda, *De temporum ratione, Epistola ad Wicthedum* : s. xi/xii, Canterbury CC.
479	12.D.xvii	Medical handbook ('Bald's Leechbook')* : s. x med., Winchester?
—	12.F.xiv, fols. 1-2, 135	[see no. **666**]
480	12.G.xii, fols. 2-9	[with Oxford, All Souls College 38, fols. I-VI and i-vi] Ælfric, *Grammar** (f) : s. xi med.
481	13.A.i	Pseudo-Callisthenes, *Historia Alexandri* (Epitome Julii Valerii) ; *Epistola Alexandri ad Aristotelem* ; Epitaphium Alexandri (W 14648) ; Alexander and Dindimus, five letters ; Recapitulatio de Alexandro : s. xi ex.
482	13.A.x, fols. 63-103	Bili of Alet, *Vita S. Machuti* (*BHL* 5116a) ; Hymn for St. Machutus (SK 1663) ; Homily for the feast of St. Machutus : s. x^2 or x/xi.
483	13.A.xi	Helperic, *De computo* ; *Dies Aegyptiaci* ; Beda, *De natura rerum, De temporum ratione* ; Treatises and excerpts on astronomical and computistical subjects (including SK 2501) ; Abbo of Fleury, *De figuratione signorum* (abbrev. from Hyginus), *De differentia circuli et sphaerae* ; Dungal, Letter to Charlemagne on eclipses (*Epist.* 1) ; Epiphanius (?) (Latin), *De mensuris et ponderibus* ; Beda, *Epistola ad Wicthedum* ; Verses on the seven liberal arts : s. xi/xii or xii in., Normandy or NW France rather than England, prob. not in England by 1100.
484	13.A.xv	Felix, *Vita S. Guthlaci* : s. x med., prob. Worcester.
485	13.A.xxii	Paulus Diaconus, *Historia Langobardorum* ; Excerpts from Josephus, *Antiquitates Judaicae* (Latin version) ; Poem on the Abbey of Saint-Bertin (SK 3639) : s. xi^2, Mont Saint-Michel, prov. Canterbury StA?, (prov. Canterbury StA).
486	13.A.xxiii	Ado of Vienne, *Chronicon* ; Lists of Roman emperors, dukes of Normandy, Frankish kings : s. xi^2, Mont Saint-Michel, prov. Canterbury StA, (prov. ibid.).
487	13.C.v	Beda, *Historia ecclesiastica* : s. x/xi or xi^1, Worcester?, (prov. Gloucester).
487.5	14.C.viii	Josephus, *De bello Judaico* (version by 'Hegesippus') : s. xi ex.
488	15.A.v, fols. 30-85	Arator, *Historia apostolica* ; Pseudo-Columbanus, *Praecepta vivendi* : s. xi ex. or xi/xii.

489	15.A.xvi	Juvencus, *Libri Evangeliorum* ; Aldhelm, *Aenigmata* ; Excerpt from Beda, *De arte metrica*, ch. xxv : s. ix$^{4/4}$ or ix/x, N France or England? *Scholica Graecarum glossarum* : s. x, England ; both parts Canterbury StA by s. x^2, (prov. ibid.).
490	15.A.xxxiii	Remigius, Commentary on Martianus Capella ; Dunchad (?Martin of Laon), Commentary on Martianus Capella, bk.viii : s. ix/x or x in., Rheims, prov. England s. x^2, (prov. Worcester).
491	15.B.xix, fols. 1-35	Sedulius, *Carmen paschale*, Hymn (SK 1904) ; Two poems on Sedulius (SK 14842, 14841) : s. x^2 or x ex., Canterbury CC.
492	15.B.xix, fols. 36-78	Latin devotional poem (f ; s. x) ; Beda, *De temporum ratione* : s. ix$^{4/4}$, Rheims area, prov. England s. x? or not in England before s. xii or xiii?
493	15.B.xix, fols. 79-199	An extensive collection of Latin verse and short prose texts, including : Symphosius, *Aenigmata* ; Beda, *De die iudicii* ; *Liber monstrorum* ; Persius, *Satirae* and anon. scholia by 'Cornutus' ; Sibylline prophecies : s. x, Rheims ; in England not before s. xii or xiii? FC : Warner and Gilson (1921), I.160-163.
494	15.B.xxii	Ælfric, *Grammar*⁺*: s. xi$^{3/4}$ or xi^2.
496	15.C.vii	Lantfred of Winchester, *Translatio et miracula S. Swithuni* ; Wulfstan of Winchester, Hymn for St. Swithun (SK 1443), *Narratio metrica de S. Swithuno* : s. x/xi ; Two poems on St. Swithun ; Legenda for Translation of St. Swithun : s. xi ex., all Winchester OM.
497	15.C.x	Vita Statii ; Statius, *Thebais* : s. x^2, Canterbury StA?, (prov. Rochester).
497.2	15.C.xi, fols. 113-194	Plautus, Eight comedies : *Amphitruo, Asinaria, Aulularia, Captivi, Curculio, Casina, Cistellaria, Epidicus* ; Isidore, *Etymologiae*, excerpt from I.xxi : s. xi/xii, Salisbury.
498	17.C.xvii, fols. 2, 3 and 163-166	Breviary (f) : s. x ex. or xi^1.

– Sloane

498.0	280, fols. 1 and 286	Homiliary (f) : s. x?

498.1	475, fols. 125-231	Isidore, *Etymologiae*, bk.IV.v ; Galen, *Epistola de febribus* ; Medical recipes ; Medical glosses ; Treatise on urines ; Gynaecological recipes ; *Somniale Danielis* (f) ; Lunarium ; *Dies Aegyptiaci* ; Prognostics : s. xi ex. or xi/xii.
—	1044, fol. 2	[see no. **21**]
—	1044, fol. 6	[see no. **648**]
498.2	1044, fol. 16	Sacramentary (f) : s. xi.
498.3	1044, fol. 21	Missal (f) : s. xi^2 or xi ex.
498.4	1086, fol. 45	Homily (f) : s. xi^2.
498.5	1086, fol. 109	Bible (f ; from Numeri) : s. xi^2.
498.6	1086, fol. 112	Sacramentary (f) : s. x/xi or xi in.
—	1086, fol. 119	[see no. **124**]
498.8	1619, fol. 2	Computus material (f) : s. x or xi, England?
498.9	2839	Medical texts, including a treatise on cauterization ; 'Petrocellus' : s. xi/xii or xii in., England or Continent.

– Stowe

499	2	Psalterium Gallicanum°, with psalter collects ; Canticles° : s. xi med. or xi$^{3/4}$, SW England, prob. Winchester NM.
500	944, fols. 6-61	Account of the history of New Minster, Winchester ; *Liber Vitae* of New Minster ; Will of King Alfred* ; Tracts on : the Six Ages of the World*, Royal Kentish saints*, Resting-places of saints* ; West-Saxon regnal list* ; Gospel lectionary (incomplete) ; Benedictions ; Lists of relics ; Pseudo-Damasus and Pseudo-Jerome, Colloquy on celebrating Mass $^{+}$* ; Gloria, Pater noster, Creeds ; Colloquy on the languages of the world : A.D.1031 and additions, Winchester NM. FC : *The Liber Vitae of the New Minster and Hyde Abbey Winchester*, ed. S. Keynes, EEMF 26 (Copenhagen, 1996).
—	1061, fol. 125	[see no. **307.2**]

– Manuscripts on permanent loan

501	Loan 11	Gospels, Gospel list (f) : c. 1020, Canterbury CC or Peterborough?, (prov. Windsor, St. George's Chapel) [Owner : Langley Marish Parish Church, Buckinghamshire].

501.2	Loan 74	Gospel of St. John : s. vii/viii, Wearmouth-J., prov. Lindisfarne, prov. Chester-le-Street, prov. Durham [Owner : The English Province of the Society of Jesus : Stonyhurst College, Whalley, Lancashire. Formerly listed as no. **756**].
501.3	Loan 81	Bible (f ; from Ecclesiasticus) : s. vii/viii, Wearmouth-J. ; prob. from the same book as no. **293** [Owner : The National Trust : Kingston Lacy, Dorset].

London, College of Arms

502	Arundel 22, fols. 84 and 85	Gospel lectionary (f) : s. $x^{4/4}$, Winchester OM?
503	Arundel 30, fols. 5-10 and 208	[palimpsest, lower script] Vergil, *Aeneid* (f) : s. $x^{2/4}$, (prov. Bury St. Edmunds).

London, Collection of S. J. Keynes Esq.

504.3	s.n.	[with Cambridge, MA., Harvard University, Houghton Library Typ 612 and Tokyo, T. Takamiya, MS 45] Benedictional (f) : s. x^{1} or x med.
504.4	s.n.	Missal (f) : s. xi med., England?

London, Lambeth Palace Library

504.8	62	Richard of Préaux, *In Genesin*, pt. i [Companion vol. to no. **162.6**] : s. xi/xii, Préaux, (prov. Canterbury CC).
505	96, fols. 2-112	Gregory, *Homiliae in Ezechielem* : s. xi ex.
506	149, fols. 1-139	Beda, *In Apocalypsin* ; Augustine, *De adulterinis coniugiis* : s. x^{2}, prov. s. xi in. SW England, prov. Exeter.
507	173, fols. 1-156	Josephus, *De bello Judaico* (version by 'Hegesippus') : s. xi/xii, (?prov. Lanthony secunda, Gloucs., Augustinian canons).
508	173, fols. 157-221	Nine Lives of Saints and Visions (incl. Beda, *Hist. eccl.* V.xii-xiv) : s. xi/xii, (prov. Lanthony secunda?). FC : James and Jenkins (1932), pp. 272-274.
508.5	173, fols. 223-232	(Pseudo-Beda), Homily for All Saints' Day : s. xi ex., (prov. Lanthony secunda?).

509	200, fols. 66-113	Aldhelm, *De virginitate* (prose) : s. x^2, Canterbury StA, prov. Barking??, (prov. Waltham Abbey, Essex, Augustinian canons).
510	204	Gregory, *Dialogi* ; Ephraem Syrus (in Latin), *De compunctione cordis* ; Rota poem (SK 11297) : s. xi^1, Canterbury CC?, (prov. Ely).
511	218, fols. 131-208	Alcuin, A selection of his letters : s. x^1 (c. 910×c.930), or s. ix ex.?, (prov. Bury St. Edmunds).
512	237, fols. 146-208	Augustine, *Enchiridion* ; Sextus Pythagoraeus (Rufinus), *Sententiae* (incomplete) : s. $ix^{2/4}$, Arras, prov. England (Glastonbury?) by s. x in.
513	325	Ennodius, *Dictiones, Epistolae, Poemata* : s. ix^2 or $ix^{3/4}$, N France? (Corbie?), (prov. Durham).
514	362, fols. 1-12	Abbo of Fleury, *Vita S. Eadmundi* ; Hymns (SK 8785, 8793) and Mass for St. Eadmund : s. xi^2 (or xi^1?), Bury St. Edmunds?, (prov. Canterbury StA?).
515	377	Isidore, *Sententiae* : s. ix^1 or $ix^{2/4}$, Tours, prov. England by s. x med., (prov. Lanthony secunda).
516	414, fols. 1-80	Excerpts from Augustine, Ambrose, Cassian, Eucherius, Jerome, etc. ; Severus, *De septem gradibus ecclesiae* ; Victorinus of Pettau, *De fabrica mundi* ; On the Seven Wonders of the World and the seven wonders of divine origin : s. ix in. or ix^1, Saint-Amand, (prov. Canterbury StA) ; in England by 1100? FC : James and Jenkins (1932), pp. 570-576.
517	427, fols. 1-202	Psalterium Gallicanum° ; Canticles° ; Form of confession° ; Prayer° ; Verse prayer* : s. xi^1, SW England (Winchester?), (prov. Lanthony secunda).
518	427, fols. 210-211	Lives of St. Mildred* (f) and Kentish royal saints* (f) : s. xi^2, Exeter?, (prov. Lanthony secunda).
—	430, flyleaves	[see no. **342.6**]
519	431, fols. 146-160	Ambrosius Autpertus, *De conflictu vitiorum et virtutum* : s. xi/xii, (prov. Lanthony secunda).
520	489	Eight homilies* (six by Ælfric) : s. $xi^{3/4}$, Exeter [one vol. with no. **322**? Companion vol. to no. **109**, pp. 3-98 and 209-224?]
520.4	1231	*Collectio canonum Hibernensis* (f) : s. ix, France (Brittany?).
520.5	1233	Alcuin, *De fide sanctae et individuae Trinitatis* (f) : s. x.

521	1370	[with London, B.L. Cotton Tiberius B.iv, fol. 87] Gospels ; Records* and writs* (s. xi^1) : s. ix^2, Ireland (prob. Armagh), prov. Canterbury CC by 924×939.

London, Public Record Office

521.4	E 31/1	Little Domesday Book : 1086-1087.
521.5	E 31/2	Great Domesday Book : 1086-1087.
521.7	SP 46/125, fol. 302	Beda, *De temporum ratione* (f) : s. x in.

London, The Schøyen Collection [see Oslo]

London, Society of Antiquaries

522	154*	Sacramentary (f) ; Lists of gospel and epistle pericopes (f) ; Two gospel pericopes : s. x^2 (or earlier, if Continental), England or Brittany?, prov. England by s. x ex., (prov. Winchester OM).

London, Wellcome Historical Medical Library

523	46	Five medical recipes* (f) : s. x/xi ; Latin poem (f ; SK 12730) : s. xi.

London, Westminster Abbey Library

523.5	17	Tract on the virtues ; Arator, *Historia apostolica* (incomplete) : s. xi/xii or xii in., England or Continent, (prov. Lincoln, Franciscan convent).
524	36, nos. 17-19	[with London, B.L. Add. 62104 and Harley 5977, no. 59 ; Lincoln Cathedral Library V.5.11 (ptd. bk.), flyleaves ; Oxford, Bodleian Library, Lat.liturg. e.38, fols. 7, 8, 13 and 14] Missal (f) : s. xi med., Exeter.

London, Westminster Abbey Muniments

524.2	67209	Homily* (f) : s. xi^1.

Longleat House, Wiltshire, Library of the Marquess of Bath

524.4   NMR 10589   Isidore, *Etymologiae* (f) : s. vii/viii, Ireland, prov. Glastonbury.
(flyleaves)

Maidstone, Kent County Archives Office

—   PRC 49/1a and b   [see no. **211**]

524.6   PRC 49/2   Haimo of Auxerre, *Homiliarium* (f) : s. xi^1.

Manchester, John Rylands University Library

524.8   109   Epistolae Pauli, with gloss by Lanfranc : s. xi ex. or xi/xii,
Canterbury CC?, (prov. Rochester?).

525   Lat.fragm.11   Pontifical (f) : s. x.

Oxford, Bodleian Library
Summary Catalogue numbers are given in brackets after the shelfmarks.

   – Arch.   [see below under Printed Books]

– Arch. Selden

—   B.26 (3340),   [see no. **346**]
fol. 34

– Ashmole

526   328 (6882 and   Byrhtferth, *Enchiridion*[+]* ; Alleluia verse (s. xi^2) : s. xi med.,
7420)   Canterbury CC?

527   1431 (7523)   Enlarged *Herbarius* (Antonius Musa, *De herba vettonica* ;
Pseudo-Apuleius, *Herbarius* ; Pseudo-Dioscorides, *Liber
medicinae ex herbis femininis*) : s. xi/xii, Canterbury StA.

– Auctarium

528   D.infra 2.9   Cassian, *De institutis monachorum* : s. x^2, Canterbury StA,
(2638),   (prov. Exeter).
fols. 1-110

528.1	D.infra 2.9 (2638), fols. 111-147	Apocalypsis, with scholia : s. xi², England?
529	D.2.14 (2698)	Gospels : s. vi ex. or vii in., Italy, prov. England (Lichfield?) s. viii ex., prov. Bury St. Edmunds s. xi?
529.1	D.2.14 (2698), fol. 173	Booklist* ; Service 'Ad introitum portae' : s. xi² or xi ex., prob. Bury St. Edmunds.
530	D.2.16 (2719)	Gospels, Gospel list : s. x¹, Landévennec (Brittany), prov. N France or Flanders, prov. England s. xi med., prov. Exeter s. xi² ; Inventory of Leofric's donations to Exeter* ; Donation inscription⁺* ; List of relics* : s. xi³/⁴, Exeter.
531	D.2.19 (3946)	Gospels° ; Poem on the Evangelists (SK 9446) : s. viii ex. or ix in., Ireland ; OE gloss s. x², N or W England.
532	D.5.3 (27688)	Gospels (incomplete) : s. ix/x, prob. Brittany, prov. England s. x.
533	F.1.15 (2455), fols. 1-77	*Vita III Boethii* ; Accessus ; Lupus of Ferrières, *De metris Boethii* ; Boethius, *De consolatione Philosophiae*, with commentary by Remigius ; Donation inscription⁺* (s. xi³/⁴) : s. x², Canterbury StA, prov. Canterbury CC s. x/xi, prov. Exeter s. xi².
534	F.1.15 (2455), fols. 78-93	Donation inscription⁺* (s. xi³/⁴) ; Persius, *Satirae*, with gloss : s. x², Canterbury StA, prov. Canterbury CC by s. x ex.?, prov. Exeter s. xi².
535	F.2.14 (2657)	Wulfstan of Winchester, *Narratio metrica de S. Swithuno* ; Prudentius, *Dittochaeon* ; Theodulus, *Ecloga* ; Avianus, *Fabulae* ; Persius, *Satirae* ; Phocas, *Ars de nomine et verbo* ; *Ilias latina* ; Pseudo-Ovid, *De nuce* ; Serlo of Bayeux, *Contra monachos* (W 15005) ; Two Latin poems (W 14029, 2123) ; Statius, *Achilleis* ; Lactantius, *De phoenice* ; Glossary⁺* (s. xii in.) : s. xi² or xi/xii, Sherborne?, (prov. Sherborne).
536	F.2.20 (2186)	Isidore, *De natura rerum* ; Cicero, *Somnium Scipionis* ; Macrobius, *In Somnium Scipionis* ; Sibylline prophecies (incomplete ; SK 8495) : s. xi ex., prov. Exeter??
537	F.3.6 (2666)	Verses on the Passion of St. Romanus (SK 5925) ; Account of Prudentius ; Prudentius, *Praefatio, Cathemerinon, Apotheosis, Hamartigenia*, 'Passio Romani' (*Peristephanon* X) ; *Psychomachia, Peristephanon, Contra Symmachum, Dittochaeon, Epilogus*, all with glosses (some OE) ; Two Charms* ; Donation inscription⁺* (s. xi³/⁴) : s. xi¹, prov. Exeter.

538	F.4.32 (2176)	fols. 1-9 : Distich by Dunstan (SK 4088) ; Eutyches, *Ars de verbo* (incomplete) : s. ix$^{2/4}$ or ix med., Brittany, prov. Wales s. x. fols. 19-36 : ('Liber Commonei') : Excerpt from Deuteronomy in Greek and Latin ; Runic alphabet ; Commentary on Coloss. ii.14-15 ; Computus material, partly in Welsh ; Notes on weights and measures ; In Greek and Latin : Biblical liturgical lessons and canticles : s. ix^1, Wales. fols. 37-47 : Ovid, *Ars amatoria* bk.i : s. ix/x (817×835), Wales. All parts prov. Glastonbury s. x^2 ; fols. 1-19 with glosses in Latin and Breton, fols. 19-47 with glosses in Latin and Old Welsh.
538.5	F.4.32 (2176), fols. 10-18	Homily (for *Inventio s. Crucis*)* : s. xi$^{3/4}$ or xi^2.

– Barlow

539	4 (6416)	Smaragdus, *Expositio libri comitis* ; Homily (xi$^{3/4}$) : s. ix$^{2/3}$, prob. NE France, prov. England by s. xi^2, (prov. Worcester).
540	25 (6463)	Juvencus, *Libri Evangeliorum* : s. x, England?
541	35 (6467)	Calendarial rules ; Prognostics ; Alcuin, *Interrogationes Sigewulfi in Genesin* ; Scholica Graecarum glossarum ; Greek-Latin Glossary ; Charm (s. xi in.) ; Pseudo-Cicero, *Synonyma* ; Glossaries$^+$* extracted from Ælfric's *Grammar* and *Glossary* (s. xi in.) : s. x, Continent, prov. England by s. xi in.

– Bodley

542	49 (1946)	Aldhelm, *De virginitate* (verse) : s. x med., (prov. Winchester OM).
543	92 (1901)	Ambrose, *De officiis ministrorum* : s. xi/xii, prob. Normandy (or England?), (prov. Exeter).
544	94 (1904)	Ambrose, *De Isaac et anima, De bono mortis, De fuga saeculi, De Jacob et vita beata, De paradiso, De obitu Valentiniani, Epistola* (extra collectionem 14 [63]) *ad Vercellensem ecclesiam* ; Jerome, *Contra Jovinianum* ; Augustine, *Epistolae* 250, 54, 209, *Sermones* 355, 356 : s. xi/xii, (England or) prob. Normandy, (prov. Exeter).
545	97 (1928)	Aldhelm, *De virginitate* (prose) : s. xi in., (prov. Canterbury CC).
546	109 (1962), fols. 1-60	Beda, *Vitae S. Cuthberti* (prose *Vita* incomplete) : s. x/xi and xi^1, Canterbury StA.

547	120 (27643), fols. i-iv	Sacramentary (f) : s. xi ex.
548	126 (1990)	Julianus Pomerius, *De vita contemplativa* : s. xi/xii, prob. Winchester OM.
548.1	126 (1990) fols. ii-iii, 60-61	Antiphons and responsories ; Office of St. Katherine ; Responsories for Office of the Dead : s. xi med. or xi^2, Winchester OM?
549	130 (27609)	Enlarged *Herbarius* (Antonius Musa, *De herba vettonica* ; Pseudo-Apuleius, *Herbarius* ; Pseudo-Dioscorides, *Liber medicinae ex herbis femininis*) ; *Curae ex hominibus* ; *Medicina de quadrupedibus* (*De taxone liber* ; Sextus Placitus, *Liber medicinae ex animalibus*) : s. xi ex., prob. Bury St. Edmunds, (prov. ibid.).
550	135 (1899)	Augustine, *Contra Faustum Manichaeum* : s. xi/xii, (England or) prob. Normandy, (prov. Exeter).
550.5	137 (1903)	Ambrose, *De apologia prophetae David*, *De Joseph patriarcha*, *De patriarchis*, *De paenitentia*, *De excessu fratris*, *Epistolae* 64-68 [74, 75, 78, 80] : s. xi ex., England, prob. Exeter (or Normandy?), (prov. Exeter).
551	145 (1915)	Augustine, *Epistolae* 200, 207, *De nuptiis et concupiscentia*, *Contra Julianum* : s. xi^2.
552	147 (1918)	Eusebius Vercellensis, *De Trinitate* ; Vigilius Thapsensis, *Contra Arianos, Sabellianos, Photinianos* ; *Epistolae* : Potamii ad Athanasium, Athanasii ad Luciferum ; Pseudo-Vigilius Thapsensis, *Solutiones obiectionum Arianorum* ; Pseudo-Jerome, *De fide catholica, Explanatio fidei ad Cyrillum* : s. xi ex., England, prob. Exeter (or Normandy?), (prov. Exeter).
553	148 (1920)	Augustine, *De consensu Evangelistarum*, with *Retractatio* II.xvi : s. xi/xii, England or Normandy, (prov. Exeter).
554	155 (1974)	Gospels, Gospel list : s. x/xi or xi in., prov. Barking ; Record* : s. xi/xii, Barking.
555	163 (2016), fols. 1-227, 250-251	Beda, *Historia ecclesiastica* ; Æthelwulf, *De abbatibus* ; Excerpts from Jerome and Orosius 'de situ Babylonis' ; Charm ; Glossary*[*] (s. xi med.) ; Caesarius, *Sermo* 216 (s. xi ex.) ; Booklist (s. xi/xii or xii in.) : s. xi in., (prov. Peterborough).
556	193 (2100)	Gregory (?), *Symbolum fidei* ; Gregory, *Registrum epistolarum* : s. xi/xii, England or Normandy, (prov. Exeter).

557	218 (2054)	Beda, *In Evangelium Lucae* ; Liturgical fragments from masses (s. x^2) : s. ix^1, Tours, prov. England by s. x.
558	223 (2106)	Gregory, *Homiliae in Ezechielem* : s. xi^2, (prov. Worcester, prov. Windsor, St. George's chapel, before s. xvi?).
559	229 (2120)	Augustine and Pseudo-Augustine, 64 *Sermones de verbis Domini, Sermo 1 de verbis apostoli* ; Caesarius, *Sermones* 154, 174 : s. x/xi or xi^1 or xi med., France, prov. Exeter.
560	237 (1939)	Florus of Lyon, *In Epistolas Pauli* : s. xi/xii, (prov. Exeter).
561	239 (2244)	Isidore, *Etymologiae* : s. xi/xii or xii in., Normandy?, (prov. Exeter).
563	301 (2739)	Augustine, *In Evangelium Johannis* : s. xi/xii, prob. Normandy, (prov. Exeter).
564	310 (2121), fols. 1-145	Gregory, *Moralia* : s. ix^2 or $ix^{3/4}$, perh. E France, prov. England before 1100 possible.
565	311 (2122)	*Judicia Theodori G* ('Canones Gregorii') ; Gregory and Augustine, *Libellus responsionum* ; *Poenitentiale Cummeani* ; *Poenitentiale Remense* ; Excerpts from *Poenitentiale Theodori* ; *Poenitentiale Oxoniense I* ; Pseudo-Jerome, *Epist. supp.* 12 ; *Poenitentiale Oxoniense II* : s. x^2, N or NW France, in England by s. x/xi, prov. Exeter by s. xi^2?
566	314 (2129)	Gregory, *Homiliae in Evangelia* : s. xi/xii, prob. Exeter, (prov. ibid.).
567	314 (2129), fols. ii, iii, 98, 99	Sacramentary (f) : s. x^1 or x^2, Brittany, (prov. Exeter).
567.5	317 (2708)	Florus of Lyon, *In Epistolas Pauli* : Ad Corinthios II - Ad Hebraeos [Companion vol. to no. **165.5**] : s. xi/xii, Préaux, (prov. Canterbury CC).
568	319 (2226)	Isidore, *De fide catholica* (ch. II.xxvii with OE gloss) : s. x^2, prob. SW England, (prov. Exeter).
569	340 (2404) and 342 (2405)	Ælfric, *Catholic Homilies** ; Homilies* ; Account of Paulinus of York* : s. xi in., Canterbury or Rochester ; additions s. xi^1 and xi med., SE England, prob. Rochester, (prov. Rochester).
570	381 (2202)	Johannes Diaconus, *Vita S. Gregorii :* s. x, England or English scribe on Continent?, prov. Canterbury StA.
570.1	381 (2202), fols. i and ii	Gospel list (part) : s. $ix^{3/4}$, prob. NE France (Corbie?), (prov. Canterbury StA).

571	385 (2210)	Jerome, *In Danielem* ; Beda, *De tabernaculo* ; Pseudo-Orosius and Pseudo-Augustine, *Dialogus quaestionum LXV* : s. xi/xii, Continent (Low Countries or NE France), (prov. Canterbury CC).
572	386 (2211), fols. i and 174	Missal (f) : s. x ex. or x/xi.
573	391 (2222)	Isidore, *De ortu et obitu patrum, Allegoriae sacrae Scripturae* ; Jerome, *De viris illustribus* ; *Decretum (Pseudo-)Gelasianum de libris recipiendis* ; Gennadius, *De viris illustribus* ; Isidore, *De viris illustribus* ; Augustine, *Retractationes* ; Cassiodorus, *Institutiones*, bk.i ; Isidore, *Prooemia Veteris et Novi Testamenti :* s. xi ex., Canterbury StA.
574	392 (2223)	31 Homilies by Eusebius Gallicanus and Caesarius, one anonymous : s. xi ex., Salisbury. FC : Webber (1992), p. 146.
575	394 (2225), fols. 1-84	Isidore, *De fide catholica* : s. x², prob. France (or England?), (prov. Exeter).
576	426 (2327), fols. 1-118	Philippus Presbyter, *Commentarii in librum Job* : 838×847, Wessex (Winchester or Sherborne?), (prov. Canterbury StA).
577	441 (2382)	Gospels* : s. xi¹ or xi¹/⁴, SE England?
578	444 (2385), fols. 1-27	Isidore, *Allegoriae sacrae Scripturae, Prooemia Veteris et Novi Testamenti, De ortu et obitu patrum* : s. xi ex., Salisbury.
578.5	447 (2680)	Beda, *De tabernaculo* : s. xi/xii or xii in.
580	479 (2013)	Beda, *De tabernaculo* : s. xi/xii or xii¹, England or France, (prov. Exeter).
581	516 (2570)	Augustine, *De videndo Deo* (*Epist.* 147) ; Ambrose, *Epistola* (extra collectionem 14 [63]) *ad Vercellensem ecclesiam* ; Halitgar, *Poenitentiale* ; Cassiodorus, *De anima* ; Excerpts from Augustine, Chrysostom, Johannes Constantinopolitanus : s. ix², N Italy or, more prob., NE France, prov. Brittany or Wales by s. x, prov. England by s. xi¹, (prov. Salisbury).
581.1	517 (2580)	William of Jumièges, *Gesta Normannorum ducum* (incomplete) : s. xi/xii Normandy, in England by 1100?
582	535 (2254), fols. 1-38	Hilduin of Saint-Denis, *Passio S. Dionysii* : s. xi³/³, Winchester OM?, (prov. ibid.)

583	572 (2026), fols. 1-50	fols. 1-25 : Mass of St. Germanus ; *Expositio Missae* ('Dominus vobiscum') ; Liber Tobias : s. x in. or x med., Cornwall. fols. 26-40 : Augustine, *De orando Deo* (Epist. 130) ; Caesarius, *Sermo* 179 ; Antiphons (s. xi/xii) ; Benedictions (s. x ex.) ; Cryptograms* (s. xi med.) ; Paschal table (s. x/xi) : s. x, Cornwall or Wales. fols. 41-50 : Colloquium (conversation lesson) '*De raris fabulis*' ; Chants for a burial office (s. x/xi), other chants, sequence (s. xi/xii) : s. x, prob. Wales. Prov. all parts Wales, s. x ex. England (Glastonbury?), s. xi prob. Winchester NM, s. xi ex. Canterbury StA.
583.3	572 (2026), fols. 51-107	Penitential collection : *Poenitentiale Cummeani* (incomplete) ; Decrees of Council of Orange (441) and other canons ; Hormisdas (?), *Epistola per universas provincias* ; Pseudo-Jerome, *Inquisitio de paenitentia* ; Injunctions concerning penitence ; Augustine of Canterbury, *Interrogatio IX* and *responsio* of Gregory (from *Libellus responsionum*) ; Prologue to *Poenitentiale Egberti* ; Pirminius, *Scarapsus (Dicta Pirminii)* : s. ix[1], prob. NE France ; in England before 1100?
584	577 (27645)	Aldhelm, *De virginitate* (verse) : s. x/xi, Canterbury CC.
585	579 (2675)	Sacramentary with catchwords for Mass chants, Pontifical, Benedictional : s. ix/x (c. 900), Saint-Vaast, Arras (or Cambrai diocese?) ; Calendar (with added obits) and computus material ('Leofric-Tiberius Computus') : prob. 979×987, Canterbury or Glastonbury? ; Pericope (and some chant) incipits : s. xi med., Exeter ; other additions made in England s. x[1] (920s) - xii, including Records* and Donation inscription[+][*] s. xi in. - s. xi ex., prov. England s. x[1/4], prov. Exeter s. xi. FC : *The Leofric Missal*, ed. F. E. Warren (Oxford, 1883).
586	596 (2376), fols. 175-214	Beda, *Vita S. Cuthberti* (prose, incomplete) ; Beda, *Vita S. Cuthberti* (verse ; part) ; *Historia de S. Cuthberto* (incomplete, s. xi/xii) ; Letald of Micy, *Vita S. Juliani* ; Chants for the office of St. Julian : s. xi ex., Durham, (prov. Canterbury StA).
587	691 (2740)	Augustine, *De civitate Dei*, with *Retractatio* II.xliii : s. xi/xii, England or Normandy, (prov. Exeter).
589	707 (2608)	Gregory, *Homiliae in Ezechielem* : s. xi ex., prob. Normandy (or England), (prov. Exeter).
590	708 (2609)	Gregory, *Regula pastoralis* ; Donation inscription[+][*] (s. xi[3/4]) : s. x ex., Canterbury CC, prov. Exeter.

591	717 (2631)	Jerome, *In Isaiam* : s. xi ex., Normandy, prob. Jumièges, (prov. Exeter).
592	718 (2632)	*Poenitentiale Egberti*, capitula i-xx, Prologue ; First Capitulary of Gerbald of Liège ; *Poenitentiale Egberti*, chs. i-xiii ; Orders of confession ; *Quadripartitus* (collection of patristic excerpts and canons), bks. 2-4 ; Excerpts from Councils (s. xi^2, xi ex.) ; Record notes (s. xi ex.) ; Prayer (s. xi/xii) ; Letter of Pope Leo IX to Edward the Confessor (s. xi$^{3/4}$) : s. x^2 or x ex., S England (Canterbury CC? Exeter? Sherborne?), prov. Exeter s. xi^2.
593	739 (2736)	Ambrose, *De fide* ; Gratianus Augustus, *Epistola ad Ambrosium* ; Ambrose, *De Spiritu Sancto, De incarnationis dominicae sacramento* : s. xi/xii, England, prob. Exeter (Normandy?), (prov. Exeter).
594	756 (2526)	Ambrosiaster, *In Epistolas Pauli* : s. xi ex., Salisbury.
594.5	762 (2536), fols. 149-226	Gratianus Augustus, *Epistola ad Ambrosium* ; Ambrose, *De fide, De Spiritu Sancto* (part) : s. xi ex., (prov. Ely?).
595	765 (2544), fols. 1-9	Augustine, *Sermones* 351 and 393 : s. xi ex., Salisbury.
595.5	765 (2544), fols. 10-77	Augustine, *De mendacio, Contra mendacium, De cura pro mortuis gerenda* ; Cyprian, *De dominica oratione* ; Ambrose, *Epistola* (extra collectionem 14 [63]) *ad Vercellensem ecclesiam* : s. xi ex., Salisbury.
596	768 (2550)	Ambrose, *De virginibus, De viduis, De virginitate, Exhortatio virginitatis* ; Nicetas of Remesiana (?), *De lapsu virginis consecratae* ; Ambrose, *De mysteriis, De sacramentis* : s. xi ex., Salisbury.
597	775 (2558)	Troper, Gradual (Cantatorium) : s. xi med., with additions s. xi$^{3/4}$ - xii in., Winchester OM. FC : Frere (1894) ; Planchart (1977).
598	783 (2610)	Gregory, *Regula pastoralis* : s. xi ex., Normandy, (prov. Exeter).
599	792 (2640)	Julian of Toledo, *Prognosticon futuri saeculi* ; Ambrose, *De virginibus, De viduis, De virginitate, Exhortatio virginitatis* ; Nicetas of Remesiana (?), *De lapsu virginis consecratae* : s. xi/xii, England or Normandy, (prov. Exeter).
600	804 (2663)	Augustine, *Contra mendacium, De natura et origine animae* : s. xi/xii or xii in., (prov. Exeter).
601	808 (2667)	Jerome, *Hebraicae quaestiones in Genesin* ; Pseudo-Jerome, *Decem temptationes populi Israel, De Hebraicis quaestionibus in libros*

Regum, in Paralipomena, In Canticum Deborae , In Lamentationes Hieremiae, De diversis generibus musicorum ; Jerome, *De situ et nominibus locorum Hebraicorum* (trans. of Eusebius, *Onomasticon*), *Liber interpretationis Hebraicorum nominum* ; Beda, *Nomina regionum locorumque de Actibus Apostolorum* : s. xi/xii, England or Normandy, (prov. Exeter).

601.5	810 (2677)	*Canones Apostolorum* ; Concilia (from Lanfranc's Collection) [Companion vol. to no. **258.3**] : s. xi ex., prob. Normandy, (prov. Exeter).
602	813 (2681)	Augustine, *In Epistolam Johannis ad Parthos* : s. xi ex. or xi/xii, England, prob. Exeter (or Normandy?), (prov. Exeter).
603	815 (2759)	Augustine, *Confessiones*, with *Retractatio* II.vi : s. xi ex., (prov. Exeter).
604	819 (2699)	Beda, *In Proverbia Salomonis* (incomplete, with additions s. x^2) : s. viii ex. or ix in. (s. viii^1?), Northumbria, prob. Wearmouth-J., prov. Chester-le-Street, prov. Durham.
605	827 (2718)	Gratianus Augustus, *Epistola ad Ambrosium* ; Ambrose, *De fide*, *De Spiritu Sancto, De incarnationis dominicae sacramento* : s. xi ex., Canterbury CC.
606	835 (2545)	Ambrose, *De Joseph patriarcha, De patriarchis, De paenitentia, De excessu fratris* : s. xi ex., Salisbury.
607	849 (2602)	Beda, *In Epistolas Catholicas* : 818, W France (Loire region?), prov. SW England s. x, Exeter s. xi.
608	865 (2737), fols. 89-96	Colloquy about the Latin language : s. xi^1, (prov. Exeter).
608.1	865 (2737), fols. 97-112	Theodulf of Orléans, *Capitula* (chs. 25-46)$^+$* : s. xi^1, (prov. Exeter).

– Broxbourne

608.5	90.28	Passion story* (f) : s. xi [formerly no. 688 in the Collection of Mr. A. Ehrman, Clobb Close, Beaulieu, Hants.].

– Digby

609   39 (1640),   Excerpt from Beda, *Historia ecclesiastica* III.vii (on St. Birinus),
           fols. 50-56   and Homily and Mass prayers for feasts of St. Birinus : s. xi^2,
                    (prov. Abingdon).

610   53 (1654), fol. 69 Antiphoner (f) : s. xi/xii, England or France?

611   63 (1664)   Computus material ('Canterbury Computus') ; Calendar ; Episcopal
                    letters and writings '*de ratione Paschali*', including Dionysius
                    Exiguus, *Epistola de ratione Paschae* : s. ix^2 (844 or 867×892),
                    Northumbria, prov. Winchester OM by s. x.

612   81 (1682),   Paschal tables ; Wandalbert of Prüm, *Horologium* (SK 14026, 8933) ;
           fols. 133-140 Poems related to the calendar (including SK 853, 8931, 1716) : s. x/xi
                    (988×1006), (prov. Durham).

613   146 (1747)   Aldhelm, *De virginitate* (prose)°, *Epistola ad Heahfridum* : s. x ex.,
                    prob. Abingdon, (prov. ibid.), most OE glosses s. xi med.

613.9 174 (1775),   Boethius, *De consolatione Philosophiae*, with gloss (f) ; Lupus of
           fol. iii   Ferrières, *De metris Boethii* (f) : s. ix, possibly in England before
                    1100.

614   175 (1776)   Beda, *Vita S. Cuthberti* (prose ; incomplete) and *Historia
                    ecclesiastica*, IV.xxix-xxx ; Miracle story from *Historia de
                    S. Cuthberto* (incomplete) ; Beda, *Vita S. Cuthberti* (verse) ;
                    Vitae S. Oswaldi, S. Aidani (both incomplete ; from Beda,
                    Historia ecclesiastica III) : s. xi/xii, Durham.

– Donation

—   f. 458   [see no. **857** ; now Arch.A.f.131 (ptd. bk.)].

– Douce

615   125 (21699)   Pseudo-Boethius, *Geometria* I ; Euclides latinus, bks. i-iv ; *Altercatio
                    duorum geometricorum* : s. x ex. or x/xi, (prov. Winchester OM).

616   140 (21714)   Primasius, *In Apocalypsin* : s. vii/viii (before 719), S England, prov.
                    Glastonbury s. x?

617   296 (21870)   Calendar ; Psalterium Gallicanum ; Canticles ; Litany ; Prayers ;
                    Office of the Trinity : s. xi$^{2/4}$, prob. Crowland.

– e Mus.

618   6 (3567)   Augustine, *In Evangelium Johannis* ; Possidius, *Vita S. Augustini* (incomplete) : s. xi ex. or xii in., Bury St. Edmunds, (prov. ibid.).

619   7 (3568)   Augustine, *In Psalmos* (101-150) : s. xi ex. or xii in., Bury St. Edmunds?, (prov. ibid.) [Companion vol. to no. **620**].

620   8 (3569)   Augustine, *In Psalmos* (50-100) : s. xi ex. or xii in., Bury St. Edmunds?, (prov. ibid.) [cf. no. **619**].

620.3   26 (3571)   Jerome, *In Prophetas minores* ; *Vita S. Macarii Romani* (added ; *BHL* 5104) : s. xi/xii, (prov. Bury St. Edmunds).

620.6   66 (3655), offsets   Arator, *Historia apostolica* (f) : s. vi or vii, prob. N Italy (or France?), (prov. Canterbury StA).

– Eng.bib., Eng.hist., Eng.th.

621   Eng.bib. c.2 (31345)   Gospels* (f ; from John) : s. xi^1.

622   Eng.hist. e.49 (30481)   Orosius, *Historiae adversus paganos** (f) : s. xi^1.

—   Eng.th. c.74   [see no. **146**]

– Fell

[623 -625]   MSS Fell 1, 3 and 4 were returned to Salisbury Cathedral Library in 1985 [see now nos. **754.5** and **754.6** (formerly nos. **625**, **623**), below ; no. **624** has been deleted].

– Hatton

626   20 (4113)   Gregory (Alfred), *Regula pastoralis** : 890×897, S England (Winchester?), prov. Worcester s. ix ex.

627   23 (4115)   Cassian, *Collationes* i-x ; Beda, *In Tobiam* : s. xi^2, prob. Worcester, (prov. Great Malvern, cell of Westminster).

628   30 (4076)   Caesarius, *In Apocalypsin* : 940×956, Glastonbury, prov. Worcester, s. x^2.

—	30 (4076), offsets from pastedowns	[see no. **636**]

629   42 (4117)   fols. 1-142 : *Collectio canonum Hibernensis* (recension B) ; *Canones Wallici* ; *Canones Adamnani* ; Gaius, *Institutiones*, bk.i ; Tables of affinity ; Notes on weights and measures, and on the parts of speech : s. ix$^{1/3}$, Brittany.
fols. 142-188 : *Collectio canonum Dionysio-Hadriana* : s. ix^1, N France?
fols. 188-204 : *Ansegisi capitularium collectio*, bk.i : s. ix med., France.
Whole MS s. x in. England, prov. Glastonbury?, prov. Canterbury CC s. x/xi, prov. Worcester by s. xi in.

630   43 (4106)   Beda, *Historia ecclesiastica* : s. xi in., Glastonbury??, prov. Canterbury CC (at least by s. xii in.).

631   48 (4118)   *Regula S. Benedicti* : s. vii ex. or viii in. or viii^1, or viii med., S England or Mercia (Worcester? possibly Bath?), prov. Worcester.

—	48 (4118), fol. 77	[see no. **653**]

632   76 (4125), fols. 1-67   Gregory (Werferth), *Dialogi** (revised version ; incomplete) ; Pseudo-Basilius (Ælfric), *Admonitio** (incomplete) : s. xi^1, Worcester?, (prov. ibid.).

633   76 (4125), fols. 68-130a   Enlarged *Herbarius** (Antonius Musa, *De herba vettonica* ; Pseudo-Apuleius, *Herbarius* ; Herbs from Pseudo-Dioscorides, *Liber medicinae ex herbis femininis* and *Curae herbarum*) ; *Medicina de quadrupedibus** (*De taxone liber* ; Treatise on mulberry tree ; Sextus Placitus, *Liber medicinae ex animalibus*) : s. xi med., Worcester?, (prov. ibid.).

635   93 (4081)   *Expositio missae* ('Primum in ordine') : s. ix^1 or ix$^{1/4}$, Mercia (Lichfield?), (prov. Worcester).

636   93 (4081), fol. 42   [with Hatton 30, offsets]
Sacramentary (f) : s. xi^1 or xi med., (prov. Worcester).

637   113 (5210)   Letter to Bishop Wulfstan II ; Prayers ; Calendar with necrology ; Computus tables ; On the Seven Ages of the World^{+}* ; Homilies* (most by Wulfstan or attrib., five by Ælfric) [Companion vol. to nos. **638** and **644**]: s. xi^2 (1064×83), Worcester.

638   114 (5134)   Homilies* (most by Ælfric) [Companion vol. to nos. **637** and **644**]: s. xi^2 (1064×83), Worcester.

639	115 (5135), fols. 1-147	[with Lawrence, University of Kansas, Kenneth Spencer Research Library, Pryce C2 :2] Ælfric, *Hexameron** ; Homilies* and sermon notes* (most by Ælfric) ; Ælfric, Homily on Judges*, *De duodecim abusivis saeculi**, (version of Alcuin's) *Interrogationes Sigewulfi in Genesin** : s. xi$^{3/4}$ or xi^2, (prov. Worcester).

– Junius

640	11 (5123)	OE Poetry : *Genesis** (A and B) ; *Exodus** ; *Daniel** (incomplete) : s. x/xi ; *Christ and Satan** : s. xi^1 ; both parts S England (Canterbury CC?).
640.1	11 (5123), offset from pastedown	Gospel harmony (f) : s. xi.
641	27 (5139)	Calendar (partly metrical) ; Psalterium Romanum° (incomplete) : s. x^1 (920s?) Winchester?, (prov. Continent by s. xii^2?).
642	85 and 86 (5196-7)	Homilies* ; Charms$^{(*)}$; *Visio S. Pauli** : s. xi med., SE England.
643	86 (5197), endleaf	Boethius (Alfred), *De consolatione Philosophiae** (f) : prob. s. x^1 or xi med. [leaf lost by 1937].
644	121 (5232)	(A version of Wulfstan's 'Handbook') : Excerpts from canons and penitentials ; Council of Winchester (1070) ; Penitential articles issued after the Battle of Hastings ; Council of Winchester (1076) ; Wulfstan, *Institutes of Polity**, '*Canons of Edgar*' *, (trans.) *Institutio canonicorum* i.145* ; *De ecclesiasticis gradibus** ; 'Benedictine Office' * ; Handbook for a confessor* ; Penitential* ('*Confessionale Pseudo-Egberti*') ; Penitential* ('*Poenitentiale Pseudo-Egberti*') ; Ælfric, Pastoral Letters I* and III* ; Homilies* (most by Wulfstan and Ælfric) [Companion vol. to nos. **637** and **638**] : s. xi$^{3/4}$ and additions s. xi^2 and s. xi ex., Worcester.

– Lat.bib., Lat.class., Lat.liturg., Lat.misc., Lat.th.

645.5	Lat.bib. b.1 (30550), fols. 73-74	Gospels (or Bible?) (f) : s. xi^1 [cf. below, 'Untraced'].
—	Lat.bib. b.2 (P) (2202*)	[see no. **448**]

646	Lat.bib. c.8 (P)	[with Salisbury, Cathedral Library, 117, fols. 163 and 164, and Tokyo, Collection of Professor Toshiyuki Takamiya, MS 21] Bible (f ; from Numeri, Deuteronomium) : s. ix^1, Mercia or S England, (prov. Salisbury).
—	Lat.bib. d.1 (P) (31089)	[see no. **770** ; this fragment was previously listed as no. **647**].
647.5	Lat.bib. d.10	Gospels (only Luke and John) : s. xi ex., prob. Normandy, (prov. Exeter).
648	Lat.class. c.2 (30551), fol. 18	[with Cambridge, Corpus Christi College, EP-0-6 (ptd. bk.), binding fragment ; Deene Park Library, L.2.21 ; London, B.L. Sloane 1044, fol. 6 ; Oxford, All Souls College 330, nos. 54 and 55] Vergil, *Aeneid* (f), *Georgica* (f) : s. $ix^{2/3}$, W France, prov. England by s. x ex.
649	Lat.liturg. d.3 (31378), fols. 4 and 5	Missal (f) : s. xi^1, Canterbury CC.
650	Lat.liturg. d.16, fol. 9	Sacramentary (f) : s. xi^2, Canterbury StA?
—	Lat.liturg. e.38, fols. 7, 8, 13 and 14	[see no. **524**]
651	Lat.liturg. f.5 (29744)	Gospel lectionary (selection for private devotion) ; Hexameter poem (s. xi ex. or xi/xii) : s. $xi^{2/4}$ or $xi^{3/4}$, England or Scotland?, prov. Scotland s. xi^2, prov. Durham s. xi ex.
—	Lat.misc. a.3, fol. 49	[see no. **436**]
651.5	Lat.th.b.2 (30588), fol. 2	Augustine, *De Trinitate* (f) : s. xi ex. or xi/xii, prob. Canterbury StA.
—	Lat.th. c.3 (31382), fols. 1, 1* and 2	[see no. **3**]
652	Lat.th. c.4 (1926*)	Sedulius, *Carmen paschale* (f), with commentary by Remigius : s. x^2, Worcester?
652.3	Lat.th. c.10, fols. 100-101a	Augustine, *In Evangelium Johannis* (f) : s. xi/xii or xii in.

—	Lat.th. d.24 (30591), fols. 1 and 2	[see no. **857**]
653	Lat.th. d.33	[with Hatton 48, fol. 77, and Oxford, St. John's College Ss.7.2, pastedown] Augustine, *Enchiridion* (f) : s. xi ex., Worcester, (prov. ibid.).
653.2	Lat.th. d.34	Tertullian, *Apologeticum* ; Pseudo-Ambrose, *De dignitate sacerdotali* ; Excerpts from Ambrose, *Expositio de Psalmo CXVIII* : s. xi/xii, Durham?

– Laud

654	Gr.35 (1119)	Actus Apostolorum (in Latin and Greek) ; Cypher alphabet (s. ix?) ; Creed, pagan oracle, Invocations to the Virgin, Edict of Flavius Pancratius of Sardinia (all in Greek) : s. vi or vii, Italy (prob. Sardinia), prov. Northumbria s. viii, prov. S Germany (Abbey of Hornbach, Palatinate) s. viii ex.
655	Lat.81 (768)	Psalterium Gallicanum ; Canticles ; Litany ; Prayers : s. xi^2, N England? Glastonbury?
656	Misc.482 (1054)	Penitential* ('*Poenitentiale Pseudo-Egberti*') ; Handbook for a confessor* ; Penitential* ('*Confessionale Pseudo-Egberti*')* ; Penitential texts* (corresponding to parts of *Poenitentiale Theodori* and *Poenitentiale Remense*) ; Manual offices (for the sick and dying)$^{(*)}$: s. xi med. or xi^2, Worcester, (prov. ibid.).
657	Misc.509 (942)	[with London, B.L. Cotton Vespasian D.xxi, fols. 18-40] Hexateuch* (part trans. Ælfric) ; Ælfric, Homily on Judges*, Letter to Wulfgeat*, Letter to Sigeweard* ; Life of St. Guthlac* : s. $xi^{3/4}$ or xi^2.
658	Misc.546 (1380)	Julian of Toledo, *Prognosticon futuri saeculi* : s. xi ex. (before 1096), Normandy, prov. Durham, (prov. Finchale).

– Marshall

659	19 (5265)	Jerome, *Liber interpretationis Hebraicorum nominum* : s. xi^1, E France? (Soissons?), prov. Malmesbury s. x^2 or x ex., (prov. Canterbury StA or CC).

– Rawlinson

—	B.484 (11831), fol. 85	[see no. **334**]

660   C.570 (12415)   Arator, *Historia apostolica* (incomplete) : s. x^2, Canterbury StA.

661   C.697 (12541)   Aldhelm, *Aenigmata* ; *Versus de alphabeto* (SK 12594) ; Aldhelm, *De virginitate* (verse), with glosses ; Prudentius, *Psychomachia* (*Praefatio* add. s. x, England) ; Acrostic poem (SK 989 ; s. x med., England) : s. ix$^{3/4}$, NE France, prov. England by s. x med. (Glastonbury?), (prov. Bury St. Edmunds).

662   C.723 (12567)   Jerome, *Homiliae in Ezechielem* : s. xi ex., Salisbury.

663   D.894 (13660),
fols. 62 and 63   Responsoriale (f) : s. x/xi.

664   G.57 (14788)
and G.111
(14836)   *Disticha Catonis* (incomplete ; with glosses from commentary by Remigius) ; *Ilias latina* ; Two Latin poems (Ovid, *Amores* 3.8.3-4, SK 8093 ; W 14116) ; *Cato novus* ; Avianus, *Fabulae* ; 'Aesopus' (Hexametrical Romulus) : s. xi ex. or xi/xii.

664.5   G.167 (14890)   Gospels (only Luke and John, both incomplete) : s. viii/ix, Ireland?

—	Q.e.20 (15606)	[see no. **355**]

– Selden supra

665   30 (3418)   Actus Apostolorum ; Prayers (s. viii or ix^1) : s. viii^1, SE England, prov. Minster in Thanet?, (prov. Canterbury StA).

—	36 (3424), fols. 73 and 74	[see no. **666**]

666   36* (3424*)   [with London, B.L. Royal 12.F.xiv, fols. 1-2, 135, and Oxford, Bodleian Library, Selden supra 36 (3424), fols. 73-74] Antiphoner (f) : s. xi^1 (xi ex.?).

– Tanner

667   3 (9823)   Gregory, *Dialogi* ; Booklist (s. xi ex. or xii in.) : s. xi in. or xi$^{2/4}$, (prov. Worcester).

668   10 (9830)   Beda, *Historia ecclesiastica** (incomplete) : s. x in. or x^1, (prov. Thorney) ; fols. 105-114 supplied s. x^2.

– Printed Books

— Arch.A.f.131 [see no. **857**]

668.5 G.1.7 Med. and Gregory, *Moralia* (f) : s. xi in.
G.1.9 Med.,
binding fragments

Oxford, All Souls College

— 38, fols. I-VI [see no. **480**]
and i-vi

— 330, nos. 54 [see no. **648**]
and 55

668.9 SR.79.g.8 Missal (f) : s. xi.
(ptd. bk.)

669 SR.80.g.8 [with Eton College 220, no. I, and Oxford, Merton College 2.f.10
(ptd. bk.) (ptd. bk.)]
Origenes (Rufinus), Homily on Leviticus (f) ; Gaudentius,
Tractatus (f) : s. xi ex.

Oxford, Balliol College

669.4 306, fols. 5-41 Boethius, *De institutione arithmetica* : s. x, France?, (prov. England).

Oxford, Brasenose College

669.6 18 *Vita Terentii* ; Terence, Comedies : *Andria, Eunuchus,
Heautontimorumenos, Adelphi, Hecyra, Phormio* : s. xi? England?

670 Latham M.6.15 Ælfric, Homily* (f : from *Catholic Homily* I.i) : s. xi[1].

Oxford, Christ Church

670.5 378, no. 24 Unidentified fragment : s. xi.

Oxford, Corpus Christi College

671	74	*Vitae III-V Boethii* ; Atticus (?), *Epistola formata* ; Lupus of Ferrières, *De metris Boethii* ; Boethius, *De consolatione Philosophiae*, with glosses from commentary by Remigius : s. xi².
672	197	*Regula S. Benedicti*ᶦ* ; Documents relating to Bury St. Edmunds Abbey (s. xi/xii) ; Records* (s. xi²) : s. x⁴/⁴, Worcester?, prov. Bury St. Edmunds by s. xi med.
673	279 pt. ii	Beda, *Historia ecclesiastica** (incomplete) : s. xi in.
673	489 no. 1	Prayers (f) : s. xi ex. or xi/xii.

Oxford, Jesus College

674	37	Johannes Diaconus, *Vita S. Gregorii* ; Four medical recipes : s. xi ex. or xi/xii, (prov. Priory of St. Guthlac, Hereford).
675	51, fol. 1	Antiphoner (f) : s. xi², (prov. Evesham?).

Oxford, Keble College

676	22	Excerpts on the Eucharist ; Epistolae Pauli, with gloss : s. xi ex., Salisbury.

Oxford, Lincoln College

677	92, fols. 165 and 166	Gospels (f) : s. viii in., Northumbria, prob. Lindisfarne.

Oxford, Magdalen College

677.3	lat. 267, fols. 60-61	[with Oslo and London, The Schøyen Collection, 79] Gregory, *Moralia* (f) : s. xi/xii or xii in., England or Continent.

Oxford, Merton College

677.5	306, fols. 5-41	Boethius, *De institutione arithmetica* : s. x, Continent?, (prov. England).
677.6	309, fols. 114-201	Commentary on the *Benedicite* ; Cicero, *Topica* (f) ; Two texts on rhetoric ; Boethius, *In Topica Ciceronis* : s. ix/x, France?

678	E.3.12	[with York, Minster Library, 7.N.10 (ptd. bk.)] Boethius, *De consolatione Philosophiae* (f) : s. x/xi.
—	2.f.10 (ptd. bk.)	[see no. **669**]

Oxford, Oriel College

680	3	Prudentius, *Praefatio*, *Cathemerinon*, *Peristephanon* ; Epigrams for the basilica of St. Agnes by Constantina (SK 2659) and Damasus (SK 4939) ; Prudentius, *Dittochaeon*, *Contra Symmachum* : s. x ex., Canterbury CC.
681	34, fols. 57-153	Beda, *In Epistolas Catholicas* : s. x, Continent, prov. England prob. s. xi².

Oxford, Queen's College

682	320	Elegiac poem on *adynata* (SK 14935) ; Isidore, *Etymologiae* : s. x med., Canterbury?

Oxford, St. John's College

684	28	'De S. Gregorio' ; Pseudo-Linus, *Martyrium S. Petri et Pauli* (*BHL* 6655) ; Gregory, *Regula pastoralis* : s. x med. or x³/⁴, prob. Canterbury StA, (prov. Abingdon s. xii?, prov. prob. Southwick, Augustinian canons, by s. xvi).
685	89	Beda, *In Apocalypsin* ; Caesarius, *In Apocalypsin* : s. xi/xii, Canterbury CC.
686	154	Ælfric, *Grammar*⁺* , *Glossary*⁺*; Four Latin Colloquies (two by Ælfric Bata ; Ælfric's *Colloquy* expanded by Bata ; abbreviated version of '*De raris fabulis*') ; Abbo of Saint-Germain, *Bella Parisiacae urbis*, bk.iii° (prose version, part, s. xi ex.) : s. xi in., (prov. Durham).
688	194	Gospels ; Parts of two Latin poems (SK 1012, 10046) in secret or Greek script ; Three prayers (*Ad pueros tonendos*, or *Ad capillaturam* ; England, s. x) : s. ix ex. or x in., prob. Brittany, prov. England s. x med., (prov. Canterbury CC).
—	Ss.7.2 (ptd. bk.), pastedown	[see no. **653**]

Oxford, Trinity College

689   4   Excerpts from Gregory of Tours, *De virtutibus S. Martini* ; Augustine, *De libero arbitrio*, *De agone Christiano* ; Gregorius Nazianzenus (Rufinus), *Liber apologeticus* (*Oratio* 2) ; [*Passio S. Mauricii sociorumque* by Marbod of Rennes : add.?] : s. x/xi?, Angers or Tours, prov. Canterbury StA prob. s. xi ex.

690   28   Beda, *De tabernaculo* ; Pseudo-Augustine, and Pseudo-Jerome, *De essentia divinitatis* ; *De ponderibus et mensuris* (from Isidore, *Etymologiae* XVI.xxv-xxvi) ; Caesarius, *De decem plagis et praeceptis* (*Sermo* 100 ; add. s. xi/xii) : s. xi (after 1066), (prov. Winchester OM).

691   39   Gregory, *Moralia*, bks. 1-10 : s. xi ex., Normandy, (prov. Lanthony secunda, Gloucs., Augustinian canons).

692   54   Augustine, *In Psalmos* (only Ps 50-72) : s. x med. or $x^{3/4}$.

692.5   60   Pseudo-Clemens (Rufinus), *Recognitiones* : s. xi ex. or xii in.

Oxford, University College

693   104   Julian of Toledo, *Prognosticon futuri saeculi* : s. xi ex., (prov. Battle).

Oxford, Wadham College

694   A.18.3   Gospels : s. xi ex.

[Redlynch, Major J.R. Abbey]

[695]   see now no. **212.2**

Ripon, Cathedral Library

696   MS.frag.2   Hymnal (f) : s. xi [binding strips in XIII d.39 (ptd. bk.); now on deposit at Leeds University Library].

Salisbury, Cathedral Library

697   6   Augustine, *Confessiones*, with *Retractatio* II.vi : s. xi ex., Salisbury.

699	9, fols. 1-60	Cyprian, *De dominica oratione, De bono patientiae, De opere et eleemosynis, De mortalitate, De catholicae ecclesiae unitate* ; Gregorius Nazianzenus (Rufinus), *De Hieremiae prophetae dictis* (*Oratio* 17) ; Caesarius, *Epistola* 2 ; Sisbertus Toletanus, *Lamentum paenitentiae* ; Exegetical dialogues and notes ; Pseudo-Jerome, *Libellus fidei* : s. xi ex., Salisbury. FC : Webber (1992), pp. 148-149.
700	10	Cassian, *Collationes* (i-x, xiv-xv, xxiv, xi) : s. xi ex., Salisbury.
700.1	10, flyleaf	Remigius, Commentary on Martianus Capella (f) : s. xi in., Continent, (prov. Salisbury).
700.2	10, flyleaf	*Liber glossarum* (f) : s. xi in., Continent, (prov. Salisbury).
701.5	12, fols. 1-56	Smaragdus, *Diadema monachorum* : s. xi ex., Salisbury.
702	24	Jerome, *In Hieremiam* : s. xi ex., Salisbury.
703	25	Jerome, *In Isaiam* : s. xi ex., Salisbury.
704	33	Gregory, *Moralia* : s. xi ex., Salisbury. [fols. 1-66 replacement leaves, s. xii^2].
706	37	Beda, *In Evangelium Lucae* : s. xi ex., Salisbury.
706.5	37, flyleaves (fols. 1-4, 165-166?)	Ambrosiaster, *Quaestiones CXXVII Veteris et Novi Testamenti* (f) : s. xi, England, prov. Salisbury.
707	38	Aldhelm, *Epistola ad Heahfridum* (incomplete), *De virginitate* (prose)° : s. x ex., Canterbury (CC or StA?).
710	63	Augustine, *De agone Christiano* with *Retractatio* II.iii, *De disciplina Christiana* ; Caesarius, *Sermo* 206 ; Theodulf of Orléans, *De processione Spiritus Sancti* ; Augustine, *De utilitate credendi, De gratia Novi Testamenti* (*Epist.* 140), *De natura boni* with *Retractatio* II.ix ; Quodvultdeus, *Adversus quinque haereses* : s. xi ex., Salisbury.
711	67	Augustine, *In Evangelium Johannis* : s. xi ex., Salisbury.
712	78	Decreta Pontificum and Concilia (Lanfranc's Collection) : s. xi ex., Salisbury.
713	88	Jerome, *De viris illustribus* ; *Decretum (Pseudo-)Gelasianum de libris recipiendis* ; Gennadius, *De viris illustribus* ; Isidore, *De viris illustribus* ; Augustine, *Retractationes* ; Cassiodorus, *Institutiones*, bk.i ; Isidore, *Prooemia Veteris et Novi Testamenti, De ecclesiasticis*

officiis I.xi-xii, *De ortu et obitu patrum*, *Allegoriae sacrae Scripturae* : s. xi ex., Salisbury.

714	89	Gregorius Nazianzenus (Rufinus), *Orationes* ; *Laudes regiae* : s. xi med., Fécamp, prov. Salisbury.
715	96	Gregory, *Dialogi* (incomplete) : s. x, Continent, or England?, prov. Salisbury.
716	101	Isidore, *Quaestiones in Vetus Testamentum* ; Adalbert of Metz, *Speculum Gregorii* (epitome of *Moralia*) ; Augustine, *In Epistolam Johannis ad Parthos* : s. ix ex., W France, prov. Canterbury CC s. x, prov. Salisbury.
717	106	Augustine, *De doctrina Christiana*, *De quantitate animae*, *Sermo* 37, Pseudo-Augustine, Easter sermon (part), Augustine, *De octo Dulcitii quaestionibus*, *De libero arbitrio*, *De natura boni*, *De vera religione*, *De disciplina Christiana* : s. xi ex., Salisbury.
—	109, fols. 1-8	[see no. **728**]
—	114, fols. 2-5	[see no. **728**]
720	114, fols. 6-122	Augustine, *De Genesi ad litteram* : s. xi ex., Salisbury.
722	117	Augustine, *De perfectione iustitiae hominis*, *De natura et gratia*, *Epistolae* 214, 215, *De gratia et libero arbitrio*, *De correptione et gratia*, *Epistolae* 225, 226, *De praedestinatione sanctorum*, *De dono perseverantiae* : s. x, Continent?, (prov. Salisbury), in England before 1100?
—	117, fols. 163-164	[see no. **646**]
724	119	Freculf of Lisieux, *Chronicon*, pt.i : s. xi ex., Salisbury.
725	120	Freculf of Lisieux, *Chronicon*, pt.i : s. xi ex., Salisbury.
728	128, fols. 1-4	[with 109, fols. 1-8, and 114, fols. 2-5] Augustine, *De Genesi ad litteram* (f) : s. xi ex., Salisbury.
729	128, fols. 5-116	Augustine, *De adulterinis coniugiis*, *De natura et origine animae* ; *Sermo Arianorum* ; Augustine, *Contra sermonem Arianorum*, *Contra adversarium legis et prophetarum* : s. xi ex., Salisbury.
730	129	Ambrosiaster, *Quaestiones CXXVII Veteris et Novi Testamenti* : s. xi ex., Salisbury.

733	132	Gregory, *Homiliae in Evangelia* : s. xi^2, (prov. Salisbury).

733 132   Gregory, *Homiliae in Evangelia* : s. xi^2, (prov. Salisbury).

734 133   Alcuin, *In Ecclesiasten* : s. ix$^{1/4}$, Tours, (prov. Salisbury).

735 134   Remigius, Commentary on Sedulius : s. x ex., England, (prov. Salisbury).

736 135   *Summa de divinis officiis* (Treatise on rites and observances of the Church) ; Isidore, *Quaestiones in Vetus Testamentum* (incomplete) : s. xi ex., Salisbury.

738 138   Augustine, *Epistolae* 200 and 207, *De nuptiis et concupiscentia*, *Contra Julianum* : s. xi ex., Salisbury.

739 140   Ambrose, *De fide*, *De Spiritu Sancto*, *De incarnationis dominicae sacramento* : s. xi ex., Salisbury.

739.5 140, fols. 1 and 2 Berengaudus, *In Apocalypsin* (f) : s. xi ex., Salisbury.

740 150, fols. 1-151 Calendar ; Computus material ; Psalterium Gallicanum° ; Canticles° : s. x^2 (prob. 969×987), SW England (Shaftesbury?), OE gloss s. xi/xii, exc. gloss to *Quicumque vult* (s. x^2).

741 154   Amalarius, *Liber officialis* ('Retractatio prima', augmented), with interpolated *Expositio missae* ('Dominus vobiscum') : s. xi ex., Salisbury.

742 157   Gregory, *Regula pastoralis* ; Office of Mary Magdalene ; Augustine, *Enchiridion*, *De orando Deo* (*Epist.* 130) ; Pseudo-Orosius and Pseudo-Augustine, *Dialogus quaestionum LXV* ; Gregory (attrib.), *De iuramentis episcoporum* ; Service for the consecration of a church ; Isidore, *Allegoriae sacrae Scripturae* ; *Prooemia Veteris et Novi Testamenti* ; *De ortu et obitu patrum* : s. xi ex., England?, (prov. Normandy s. xiii in.).

743 158, fols. 1-8 Helperic, *De computo* : s. xi med., France, prov. Salisbury by s. xi ex.

744 158, fols. 9-83 Computus tables ; Beda, *De temporum ratione* : s. ix^2 or ix/x, France, prov. Salisbury by s. xi ex.

745 159   Origenes (Rufinus), *In Exodum*, *In Leviticum* : s. xi ex., prov. Salisbury.

747.5 162, fols. 1-2, 29-30 Berengaudus, *In Apocalypsin* (f) : s. xi ex., Salisbury.

748 164, fols. 64-129 Ivo of Chartres, *Sermones* : s. xi ex. or xi/xii.

749	165, fols. 1-87	Vigilius Thapsensis, *Contra Felicianum* ; Pseudo-Methodius, *Revelationes* ; Beda, *De tabernaculo* ; Hrabanus Maurus, 'De ponderibus', 'De mensuris', from *De universo* : s. xi ex., Salisbury.
749.5	165 fols. 122-178	Alcuin, *De fide sanctae et individuae Trinitatis, De Trinitate ad Fredegisum, quaestiones XXVIII, De animae ratione* ; Gennadius, *Liber ecclesiasticorum dogmatum* ; *Decretum (Pseudo-)Gelasianum de libris recipiendis* ; Pseudo-Jerome, *De duodecim scriptoribus* ; Two Eucharistic miracle stories : s. xi ex., Salisbury.
750	168	Augustine, *De diversis quaestionibus LXXXIII* ; *De duodecim abusivis saeculi* ; Beda, *De die iudicii* : s. xi ex., Salisbury.
750.5	169, fols. 1-77	Augustine, *De utilitate agendae paenitentiae* (*Sermo* 351), *Sermo* 393, *De disciplina Christiana, Sermo* 37, *De octo Dulcitii quaestionibus, Epistola* 130 ; Pseudo-Orosius and Pseudo-Augustine, *Dialogus quaestionum LXV* ; Pseudo-Augustine, Easter Sermon (part) ; Vigilius Thapsensis, *Contra Felicianum* : s. xi ex., Salisbury.
751	172	Augustine, *Enchiridion* : s. x[2], prob. Canterbury.
752	173	Augustine, *Soliloquia* ; Isidore, *Synonyma* : s. x ex., Continent, prov. England, (prov. prob. Salisbury.).
753	179	Paulus Diaconus, *Homiliarium* (Easter to All Saints and Commune SS.) : s. xi ex., Salisbury.
754	180	Psalterium Gallicanum and Hebraicum ; Canticles ; Litany ; Prayers : s. ix/x, N France or Brittany, prov. England s. x[1], (prov. Salisbury).
754.5	221	Office legendary (January-June) [Companion vol. to no. **754.6** and ?no. **215**] : s. xi ex., Salisbury [ex Bodl. Fell 4]. FC : Webber (1992), pp. 154-156.
754.6	222	Office legendary (July-December ; now incomplete, ends Oct. 9) [cf. no. **754.5**] : s. xi ex., Salisbury [ex Bodl. Fell 1]. FC : Webber (1992), pp. 156-157.

Shrewsbury, Shropshire Record Office

755	1052/1	Jerome, *In Evangelium Matthaei* (f) : s. viii[2], prob. Northumbria.

Shrewsbury, Shrewsbury School

755.5	21	Gregory, *Regula pastoralis* : s. xi/xii, Normandy, (prov. Durham).

Stonyhurst College, Lancashire, Society of Jesus

[756]   [see now no. **501.2**]

756.5   5.50 (ptd. bk.)   Missal (f) : s. xi².

Ushaw, Co. Durham, St. Cuthbert's College

757   44   Office lectionary (f) : s. viii med., Northumbria.

Wells, Cathedral Library

758   7   Regula S. Benedicti⁺* (f) : s. xi med.

Winchester, Cathedral Library

759   1   [with London, B.L. Cotton Tiberius D.iv, vol. ii, fols. 158-166]
Beda, *Historia ecclesiastica* ; Æthelwulf, *De abbatibus* ; Excerpts from Jerome and Orosius 'de situ Babylonis' : s. x/xi or xi in., (prov. Winchester).

Winchester, Winchester College

759.5   40A   Basil (Rufinus), *Homiliae in Psalmos* (f) : s. viii², France?

Windsor, St. George's Chapel

760   5   Gregory, *Homiliae in Ezechielem* ; Beda, *In Proverbia Salomonis* : s. xi/xii, (prov. s. xii Canterbury CC).

Worcester, Cathedral Library

761   F.48   A collection of texts from *Vitas Patrum* :
fols. 1-48 : Jerome, *Vita S. Pauli Eremitae* ; Athanasius (Evagrius), *Vita S. Antonii* ; Jerome, *Vita S. Hilarionis* : s. xi ex., prov. Worcester.
fols. 49-104 : Rufinus, *Historia monachorum* : s. xi¹, Continent?
fols. 105-164 : 171 selections from *Verba seniorum* ; *Vita Thais* (incomplete ; s. xii?) : s. x/xi or xi in. or xi med., Worcester or York. Whole MS prov. Worcester.

761.5   F.72, flyleaves   Gospels (f : Canon table) : s. ix¹ (decoration later?).

762	F.91	Smaragdus, *Expositio libri comitis* : s. x$^{3/4}$, prob. Worcester, (prov. ibid.).
763	F.92	Paulus Diaconus, *Homiliarium* (Advent to Easter) [Companion vol. to nos. **763.1** and **763.2**] : s. xi/xii or xii in., prov. Worcester. FC : Schenkl (1891-1908), no. 4320.
763.1	F.93	Paulus Diaconus, *Homiliarium* (Easter to Advent) [cf. no. **763**] : s. xi/xii or xii in. FC : Schenkl (1891-1908), no. 4321.
763.2	F.94	Paulus Diaconus, *Homiliarium* (Sanctorale, 3 May - 30 Nov., and Commune SS.) [cf. no. **763**] : s. xi/xii or xii in. FC : Schenkl (1891-1908), no. 4322.
764	F.173	Missal (part) : s. xi med., Winchester OM, prov. Worcester?
764.1	F.173, fol. 1	Psalterium Gallicanum (f), with gloss : s. x^2.
765	Q.5	Beda, *De arte metrica* ; Inscription (SK 1479) ; Beda, *De schematibus et tropis* ; Priscian, *Institutio de nomine, pronomine et verbo* ; Grammatical texts and glosses ; Two glossarial poems on Greek medical terminology (SK 13822 and 3618 ; 11969) ; Israel the Grammarian, *De arte metrica* (SK 14392) ; Verses by Alcuin (from *carm.* 80.1, SK 11084) ; '*Pauca de philosophiae partibus*' ; Table of metrical feet ; Charm$^{(*)}$ (s. xi med.) : s. x ex., Canterbury CC, (prov. Worcester).
766	Q.8, fols. 165-172	[with Add.7, fols. 1-6] Statius, *Thebais*, glossed (f) : s. ix/x, France? s. x/xi or xi in. England?, (prov. Worcester).
767	Q.21	Gregory, *Homiliae in Evangelia* : s. x/xi or xi in., France, prov. England by s. xi/xii, prob. Worcester.
768	Q.28	Eusebius (Rufinus), *Historia ecclesiastica* : s. ix^2, France, prov. s. xi (or x^2?) England, (prov. Worcester).
769	Q.78B	Office lectionary (f) : s. x in., N France, (prov. Worcester).
770	Add.1	[with Oxford, Bodleian Library, Lat. bib. d. 1 (P)] Gospels (f) : s. viii ex. or ix in., perh. Canterbury (StA), or Worcester?
770.5	Add.2	Jerome, *In Evangelium Matthaei* (f) : s. vii, prob. Spain, prov. prob. Worcester s. viii.
771	Add.3	Gregory, *Regula pastoralis* (f) : s. viii.

772	Add.4	Paterius, *De expositione Veteris et Novi Testamenti* (f) : s. viii.
773	Add.5	Isidore, *Sententiae* (f) : s. viii^2.
—	Add.7, fols. 1-6	[see no. **766**]

Wormsley, nr. Stokenchurch (Buckinghamshire), The Wormsley Library (Collection of Sir John Paul Getty)

773.5	s.n.?	Eusebius (Rufinus), *Historia ecclesiastica* (f) : s. vii (s. vii^1 or vii med.), Northumbria or Ireland (or Continent?), prov. England s. vii or later.

York, Minster Library

773.6	XVI.Q.1	Gregory, *Moralia*, bks. 1-10 [Companion vol. to no. **773.7**] : s. xi ex. or xi/xii, (prov. York?).
773.7	XVI.Q.2	Gregory, *Moralia*, bks. 11-22 [Companion vol. to no. **773.6**] : s. xi/xii or xii in., (prov. York?).
774	Add.1, fols. 10-161	Gospels : s. x ex. - xi in., Canterbury CC?, prov. York (by 1020-1023) ; Records* (s. xi^1, xi^2) ; Three short sermons (tracts)* by Wulfstan ; Writ of King Cnut* ; Prayers* : s. xi^1, York ; List of service-books : s. xi med.
—	VII.N.10 (ptd. bk.)	[see no. **678**]

Addendum

London, Collection of R. A. Linenthal Esq.

774.1	s.n.	Gregory of Tours, *De virtutibus S. Martini* (f) : s. xi^1.

II. Libraries outside the British Isles

Alençon, Bibliothèque Municipale

774.3   14, fols. 91-114   Benedictional ; Two masses *de amico* : s. xi^1, Winchester, prov. Saint-Évroult.

Amiens, Bibliothèque Municipale

774.6   377, flyleaves   Sacramentary (f) : s. x, England?

Antwerp, Plantin-Moretus Museum

775   M.16.2 (47)   [with London, B.L. Add. 32246]
Excerptiones de Prisciano : s. xi^1, prob. Abingdon (or Continent?). Additions at Abingdon : (1.) Three glossaries (one Latin-OE) : s. xi in. ; (2.) Remigius, Commentary on Donatus ; Ælfric, *Colloquy* (incomplete) ; Four poems, three on English saints and Archbishop Ælfric ; Poem addressed to Abbot Wulfgar of Abingdon (W 18791) : all s. xi^1.

776   M.16.8 (190)   Boethius, *De consolatione Philosophiae*, with commentary by Remigius : s. x/xi, Abingdon.

776.2   M.16.15 (194)   Gospels : s. xi^1, Canterbury??

Arendal, Aust-Agder Arkivet

777   A.A.69 and 77   [with Rygnestad, Archives of Ketil Rygnestad, no. 95, and Archives of Knut Rygnestad, no. 99]
Antiphoner (f) : s. xi$^{1/3}$, or earlier?

Arras, Bibliothèque Municipale (Médiathèque)

778   346 (867)   Ambrose, *Hexameron* : s. x/xi or xi in., prob. Abingdon, supplemented s. xi med., prob. Exeter, prov. Bath, prov. Saint-Vaast, Arras.

779   764 (739),   Hrabanus Maurus, *In Judith, In Hester* : s. ix ex., NE France, prov.
          fols. 1-93   England s. x, prov. Bath, prov. Saint-Vaast, Arras.

780   764 (739),   Isidore, *Allegoriae sacrae Scripturae, Prooemia Veteris et Novi*
          fols. 134-181   *Testamenti, De ortu et obitu patrum* : s. ix/x, Winchester?, prov. Bath by s. xi, prov. Saint-Vaast, Arras.

781	1029 (812)	Anon., *Vita S. Cuthberti* (incomplete ; *BHL* 2019) ; Felix, *Vita S. Guthlaci* (incomplete) ; *Vita S. Dunstani* by 'B' (incomplete ; *BHL* 2342) ; *Vita S. Philiberti* (incomplete ; *BHL* 6805) ; *Vita S. Aichardi* (incomplete ; *BHL* 181) : s. x ex. and xi in., prov. Bath, prov. Saint-Vaast, Arras.

Note : The following manuscripts were among the books given by Sæwold, former abbot of Bath, to the church of Saint-Vaast, Arras (cf. Lapidge (1985), pp. 58-62 ; repr. 1994, pp. 125-30) ; but there is no proof that they were ever in England : Arras B.M. 435 (326), fols. 65-122 ; 644 (572) ; 732 (684) ; 899 (590) ; 1068 (276) ; 1079 (235), fols. 28-80. See also no. **808.2**.

Avranches, Bibliothèque Municipale

782	29	55 Homilies ; Two prayers to the Virgin (s. xi) ; ('Martinellus') : Sulpicius Severus, *Vita S. Martini* (f) ; Excerpts from Gregory of Tours, *Historia Francorum* and *De virtutibus Sancti Martini* ; Sulpicius Severus, *Epistola* III : s. x/xi, S England, prov. Mont Saint-Michel.
—	48, fols. i and ii, 66, fols. i and ii, 71, fols. A and B	[see no. **842**]
783	81	Augustine, *In Epistolam Johannis ad Parthos* ; Pseudo-Eusebius Gallicanus, *Sermo* 12 ; Alcuin, *De virtutibus et vitiis* ; Augustine and Pseudo-Augustine, five sermons (including *Sermones* 85, 74, 79, 68) : s. xi², England or NW France?, prov. Mont Saint-Michel.
784	236	Boethius, *De institutione musica* ; Excerpts from Beda, *De arte metrica* and *De temporum ratione* ; Conversation phrases in Latin and Greek : s. x/xi, prov. Mont Saint-Michel by s. xi ex.

Bamberg, Staatsbibliothek

784.5	Msc.Ph.1 (HJ.IV.16)	Alcuin, *carm.* 77.1, *De dialectica* ; Anon. poem ; Porphyrius (Boethius), *Isagoge* ; Pseudo-Apuleius, *Peri hermenias* ; Isidore, *Etymologiae* II.xxix-xxxi ; '*De divisione philosophiae*' : s. x, Brittany (or England?), (prov. Bamberg Cathedral).

Basel, Universitätsbibliothek

785	F.III.15b, fols. 1-19	Pseudo-Isidore, *De ordine creaturarum* : s. viii[1], prob. Northumbria, prov. Fulda.

786	F.III.15f	Isidore, *De natura rerum* : s. viii[1] or viii med., England, prov. Fulda.
787	F.III.15l	Isidore, *Differentiae* ; Gennadius, *Liber ecclesiasticorum dogmatum* : s. viii[1], England, prov. Fulda.
788	N.I.2, fol. 1	Psalterium Romanum (f) : s. viii.

Bergen, Universitetsbiblioteket

789	1549.5	Missal (f) : s. xi/xii.

Berlin, Staatsbibliothek Preussischer Kulturbesitz

790	Hamilton 553	Psalterium Romanum ; Canticles : s. viii[1], Northumbria, prob. Lindisfarne, (prov. Nunnery of Saint-Jean, Laon, c. 1120).
791	Lat.fol. 877	[with Hauzenstein near Regensburg, Gräflich Walderdorffsche Bibliothek, s.n., and Regensburg, Bischöfliche Zentralbibliothek, Cim 1] Calendar (f) ; Sacramentary (f) : s. viii med., Northumbria, prov. Regensburg s. viii.
791.3	Theol.lat.fol. 355, binding fragment	Saints' lives (f) : s. viii[2], S England, or Werden, prov. Werden. [and other fragments in Berlin, Bonn and Düsseldorf? Cf. Bischoff 1998, no. 458, and B. Barker-Benfield, *ASE* 20 (1991), 54 and n. 48].
791.6	Fragm. 34	Wigbod (Pseudo-Beda), *Quaestionum super Genesin dialogus* (f) : s. viii, prob. England, prov. Werden.
791.9	Grimm 132,1	[with Budapest, National Széchényi Library, Cod.lat. 441, fols. 1 and 2 ; Budapest, University Library, Fragm.lat. 1 ; München, Stadtarchiv, Historischer Verein Oberbayern, Hs. 733/16] Beda, *Vita S. Cuthberti* (verse) (f) : s. viii[2] or viii/ix, S England or Germany (Rhine-Main area? Fulda?).
792	Grimm 132,2	[with Grimm 139,2] Excerpts from Augustine, *In Psalmos* (f) ; Biblical and other glosses (f) : s. viii med., England or Germany?
793	Grimm 139,1	Pelagius, *In Epistolam Pauli ad Philippenses* (f) : s. viii[1], Northumbria.
—	Grimm 139,2	[see no. **792**]

Bern, Burgerbibliothek

794 671 Gospels ; Two acrostic poems addressed to King Alfred (SK 302, 4458 ; s. x in.) ; Records* (s. x^1 or x med.) : s. ix^1, SW England, Cornwall, or Wales, prov. Great Bedwyn, Wiltshire s. x^1, prov. France by s. xi/xii.

794.5 680 Augustine, *Enchiridion* : s. x ex.

795 C.219(4) [with Leiden, Bibliotheek der Rijksuniversiteit, Voss.lat. Q.2, fol. 60] Themistius, *De decem categoriis* ; Porphyrius (Boethius), *Isagoge* (f) : s. ix ex., Wales, or SW England?, (prov. Fleury?).

Besançon, Bibliothèque Municipale

796 14 Gospels : s. x ex. (c. 980-90), or xi in.?, Winchester NM?, (prov. Abbey of Saint-Claude, French Jura, by s. xii ex.).

Bloomington, Indiana University, Lilly Library

— Add. 1000 [see no. **441**]

— Poole 40 [see no. **146**]

796.3 Poole 41 Missal (f) : s. x^2 or x ex.

796.6 Poole 43 Anso of Lobbes, *Vita S. Ermini* (f ; *BHL* 2614) : s. xi ex. or xi/xii.

Boulogne-sur-Mer, Bibliothèque Municipale

798 10 Gospels : s. x^1 or x med., S England?, (prov. Saint-Vaast, Arras).

799 32 (37) Ambrose, *De apologia prophetae David*, *De Joseph patriarcha*, *De patriarchis*, *De paenitentia*, *De excessu fratris*, *Epistolae* 64-68 [74, 75, 78, 80, 26] : prob. Italy s. vi^1, prov. prob. England s. viii, (prov. Saint-Bertin).

799.5 58 (63 and 64) Augustine, *Epistolae* 187 and 54 (?) : s. viii^2 or viii^1, prob. England, (prov. Saint-Bertin).

800 63 (70), Excerpts from Julian of Toledo, *Prognosticon futuri saeculi* ;
fols. 1-34 Ælfric, Pastoral Letter 2a ; Anon. Sermon (by Ælfric?) ; Gregory, *Regula pastoralis* I.ix ; Excerpts from works of Isidore and Jerome ; *De ecclesiasticis gradibus* ; *Decretum (Pseudo-)Gelasianum de libris recipiendis* ; Caesarius, *Sermo* 51 ; *Decalogus Moysi* with exposition ;

Pseudo-Eusebius Gallicanus, *Sermo* 12 : s. xi[1], England, (prov. Saint-Bertin).
FC : E. M. Raynes, *MÆ*, 26 (1957), 65-73.

801	63 (70), fols. 35-86	Caesarius, *In Apocalypsin* ; Augustine, *Epistolae* 166, 205 ; Pseudo-Augustine, *De symbolo* : s. x, France, prov. S England by s. x med., (prov. Saint-Bertin).
802	74 (82)	Apponius, *In Canticum canticorum* (abridged ; incomplete) ; Letter by Burginda : s. viii[1], S England or Mercia (Bath?), (prov. Saint-Bertin by s. xii in.).
803	82	Amalarius, *Liber officialis* ('Retractatio prima') : s. x[1], (prov. Saint-Bertin).
804	106 (127), fols. 1-92, 119-171	*Vita S. Walarici* (*BHL* 8762) ; *Vita S. Philiberti* (*BHL* 6805) ; *Vita S. Aichardi* (*BHL* 181) ; *Vita S. Bavonis* (f ; *BHL* 1049) ; Felix, *Vita S. Guthlaci* ; Seven homilies : s. x/xi, prov. Bath?, (prov. Saint-Bertin).
804.5	106 (127) (binding strip)	Gregory, *Homiliae in Evangelia* (f) : s. viii-ix, prob. England, (prov. Saint-Bertin).
805	189	Sibylline prophecies (SK 8495) ; Poem (excerpt from Porphyrius Optatianus, *carm.* 25 ; SK 1005) ; Prefatory letter to Frithegod's *Breviloquium Vitae Wilfridi* ; Collection of drinking-verses (SK 4819) ; Prudentius, *Praefatio°*, *Cathemerinon°*, *Peristephanon°*, *Contra Symmachum°* ; *Epilogus°* : s. x/xi, Canterbury CC, OE glosses s. xi in., xi[1], (prov. Saint-Bertin).

Braunschweig, Stadtbibliothek

—	Fragm. 70	[see no. **856**]

Brussels, Bibliothèque Royale

805.5	444-52 (1103)	Augustine, *De perfectione iustitiae hominis, De natura et gratia, De gratia et libero arbitrio, De correptione et gratia* ; Prosper, *Pro Augustino responsiones ad capitula obiectionum Gallorum* ; Hilarius (?), *Epistola ad Augustinum de querela Gallorum* ; Augustine, *De praedestinatione sanctorum, De dono perseverantiae* ; Pseudo-Augustine, *Hypomnesticon* ; Jerome, *Contra Jovinianum* : s. xi/xii, Canterbury StA.
806	1650 (1520)	Aldhelm, *De virginitate* (prose)° : s. xi in., Abingdon, Latin and OE glosses s. xi[1].

807	1828-30 (185), fols. 36-109	*Hermeneumata Pseudo-Dositheana* ; Glossaries, including five Latin-OE class lists ; Treatise on dialectic ; Library catalogue (s. xi/xii) : s. xi in., prov. s. xi/xii Abbey of Anvin near Douai.
808	8558-63 (2498)	fols. 1-79 : Chrodegang, *Regula canonicorum* (enlarged version ; incomplete) ; Augustine, *Soliloquia* ; Caesarius, *Sermo* 179 : s. x^1, S England or Mercia. fols. 80-131 : *Poenitentiale Pseudo-Theodori* (incomplete) : s. x med. fols. 132-153 : Handbook for a confessor* ; Penitential (*'Poenitentiale Pseudo-Egberti'*), bk.iv* ; Penitential texts* : s. xi^1.
808.1	8794-99 (1403), fols. 1-17	Ernulf of Rochester, *De incestis coniugibus* ; Decretum : s. xi/xii? Rochester.
808.2	9850-52	fols. 4-139 and 144-176 : *Verba seniorum* i-xv.39 (*Vitas Patrum*, bk. V) ; Caesarius, *Sermones* ; *Decretum (Pseudo-)Gelasianum de libris recipiendis* ; Commentary on the Gospels : s. vii/viii, Soissons, prov. Corbie s. viii ex.? fols. 140-143 : Caesarius, *Sermo* 23 : s. viii ex., Corbie area. Whole MS prov. Bath?, prov. Saint-Vaast, Arras by s. xi^2 [cf. note after no. **781**].
808.3	II.436	Gospels (f) : s. viii, England.
808.4	II.1766, fol. 2	Unidentified text (f) : s. ix or x in.

Bückeburg, Niedersächsisches Staatsarchiv

—	Depot 3/1	[see no. **856**]

Budapest, National Széchényi Library

—	Cod.Lat.441, fols. 1-2	[see no. **791.9**]

Budapest, University Library

—	Fragm.lat.1	[see no. **791.9**]

Cambrai, Bibliothèque Municipale

808.5	470 (441)	Philippus Presbyter, *Commentarii in librum Job* : s. viii^1 or viii med., prob. English.

Cambridge, Mass., Harvard University, Houghton Library

—   Typ 612   [see no. **504.3**]

Châlons-en-Champagne (Châlons-sur-Marne), Archives de la Marne

808.6   Fragm.I.7   Psalterium Romanum (f) : s. x^2.

Chicago, Newberry Library

808.7   fragm.15   Alcuin, *Epistolae* (f ; from *Epist.* 149,155,136) : s. $x^{2/4}$.

Christchurch, New Zealand, private collector

808.9   s.n.?   Prudentius, *Contra Symmachum*, with gloss (f) : s. x/xi, Canterbury, prob. CC.

Coburg, Landesbibliothek

809   1   Gospel list, Gospels : s. $ix^{2/3}$ Metz, prov. England (royal court) c. 923×936?, prov. Gandersheim by s. xi in.

Cologne (see Köln)

Columbia, University of Missouri, Ellis Library, Fragmenta manuscripta

809.8   F.M.1   Office lectionary (f) : s. x med. or x^2, Brittany?, prov. England by s. x ex.

809.9   F.M.2   Excerpts from : Beda, *De orthographia*, Priscian, *Institutio de nomine, pronomine et verbo*, and *Institutiones grammaticae* ; Audax, *Excerpta* : s. ix, prob. Wales, prov. Winchester by s. x in.

810   F.M.3   Sacramentary (f) : s. x/xi.

811   F.M.4   Excerpts from Old Testament Minor prophets (f) : s. x^2.

Copenhagen, Det Arnamagnaeanske Institut

811.5   s.n.   Ælfric, Homilies* (f : from enlarged First Series of *Catholic Homilies*) : prob. s. xi¹ [prob. from the same MS as nos. **816.6** and **830**].

Copenhagen, Kongelige Bibliotek

812   G.K.S.10 (2°)   Gospels : s. x ex. or xi in.?, Winchester NM? or Peterborough?, prov. s. xi Peterborough or Canterbury, (prov. : had left England by s. xii ex.?).

813   G.K.S.1588 (4°)   Abbo of Fleury, *Vita S. Eadmundi* ; Office of St. Eadmund (incomplete) : s. xi⁴⁄⁴, Bury St. Edmunds, prov. s. xi ex. Saint-Denis?

814   G.K.S.1595 (4°)   (A version of Wulfstan's 'Handbook') : Amalarius (?) , *Eclogae de ordine Romano* ; Excerpts from Isidore and Jerome ; *De ecclesiasticis gradibus* ; Wulfstan (?), Two sermons ; Abbo of Saint-Germain, *Sermones* 6-13 ; Letters relating to penitence by Wulfstan and by Pope John XVIII ; Fifteen sermons (including Wulfstan Ia and VIIIa) ; Excerpts from Scripture by Wulfstan ; Ælfric, Pastoral Letters 2 and 3 ; *De officio missae* : c. 1002-1023, Worcester (and York?), prov. Denmark (Roskilde) s. xi?
FC : *The Copenhagen Wulfstan Collection*, ed. J. E. Cross and J. Morrish Tunberg, EEMF 25 (Copenhagen, 1993).

815   G.K.S.2034 (4°)   Beda, *Vita S. Cuthberti* (verse, incomplete)° ; Pseudo-Columbanus, *Praecepta vivendi* : s. x/xi, OE glosses s. xi¹.

816   N.K.S.167b (4°)   *Waldere** (f) : s. x/xi.

Copenhagen, Rigsarkivet

– Middelalderlige Håndskriftfragmenter

—   3084 and 3085   [see no. **872**]

816.3   3185 and 3186   Missal (f) : s. xi.

—   4593   [see no. **871**]

– Aftagne Pergamentfragmenter

816.6   637-664, 669-   Ælfric, *Catholic Homilies** (f ; from I.xxvi and xxxv-xxxvii) : s. xi¹
        671, 674-698   [Fifty-six binding strips, prob. from the same MS as nos. **811.5** and **830**].

[Damme, Musée van Maerlaut]

[817]   see now no. **848.8**

Darmstadt, Hessische Landes- und Hochschulbibliothek

818   4262   Beda, *De temporum ratione* (f) : s. viii¹, Wearmouth-J.

Düsseldorf, Nordrhein-Westfälisches Hauptstaatsarchiv

820   Z 11/1   Orosius, *Historiae adversus paganos* (f) : s. viii², prob. Northumbria
                                   [formerly Z.4, Nr. 2].

Düsseldorf, Universitätsbibliothek

All fragments are on permanent loan from the Hauptstaatsarchiv ; all shelfmarks have been changed.

818.5   Fragm.   [with San Marino, California, Henry E. Huntington Library RB 99513
         K1 : B 210   (PR 1188 F)]
                                   Isidore, *De ortu et obitu patrum* (f) ; *Allegoriae sacrae Scripturae* (f) :
                                   s. viii² or viii ex., prob. England, or Werden? [formerly B.210].

819   Fragm.   Johannes Chrysostomus (in Latin), *De reparatione lapsi* (f),
         K1 : B 215,   *De compunctione cordis* (f) ; *Passio S. Justi pueri* (f) ; *Pastor*
         K2 : C 118   *Hermas* (f) : s. viii med., prob. Northumbria [formerly B.215, C.118].
         and K15 : 00

821   Fragm.   [with Gerleve, Abteibibliothek, s.n.]
         K 15 : 017 and   Isidore, *Etymologiae* (f) : s. viii², prob. Northumbria [formerly Z.4,
         K 19 : Z8/7b   Nr. 3, and Fragm. 28].

822   Fragm.   Cassiodorus, *In Psalmos* (abbrev., f) : s. viii¹, Northumbria [formerly
         K16 : Z.3/1   s.n., then Z.3/1].

El Escorial, Real Biblioteca

823   E.II.1.   Boethius, *De consolatione Philosophiae*, with abbreviated version
                                   of commentary by Remigius : s. x/xi or xi in., Continent or England,
                                   prov. Horton, Dorset, s. xi².

Épinal, Bibliothèque Municipale

824	72 (2), fols. 94-107	Glossary[+]* : s. vii ex. or vii/viii.

Évreux, Bibliothèque Municipale

824.5 43 Proba, Preface to *Cento Vergilianus* (SK 14383) ; Sedulius, Letter I to Macedonius, *Carmen paschale* with glosses, Hymns : s. x, England?, (prov. Lyre, Normandy).

Florence, Biblioteca Medicea Laurenziana

825 Amiatino 1 Bible : s. vii ex. or viii in. (before 716), Wearmouth-J., prov. Continent s. viii, prov. Abbey of Monte Amiato, Italy (by s. ix or x?).

827 Plut.xvii.20 Gospel lectionary : s. $xi^{2/4}$, Canterbury CC?, prov. Continent s. xi.

Freiburg i.B., Universitätsbibliothek

827.2 702, fol. 1 Gospels (f) : s. viii^1, Northumbria or Continent (Echternach?).

Fulda, Hessische Landesbibliothek

827.5 Aa.21 Gospels : s. xi (1051×1064) and Continent 1065×1071, prov. Bavaria c. 1071, prov. Weingarten s. xi ex.

827.6 Codex Bonifatianus 1 New Testament, including Tatian, *Diatessaron* (in Latin, rev. by Victor of Capua) : s. vi^1 (before 546 or 547), S Italy, prov. England s. viii^2, prov. Germany.

827.7 Codex Bonifatianus 3 Gospels : s. viii^2 or viii/ix, Ireland, prov. S England?, prov. Germany.

Geneva (Cologny-Genève), Bibliotheca Bodmeriana

828 2 Ælfric, *Catholic Homily* II.v* (f) : s. xi^2.

829 175 Lupus of Ferrières, *De metris Boethii* ; Boethius, *De consolatione Philosophiae*, with commentary by Remigius ; Donatus, *Ars maior* I (excerpt) ; Latin poems (including SK 638, 13123, 11355) : s. x^2 or xi in., Canterbury??

125

Gerleve, Westphalia, Abteibibliothek

829.2   s.n.   Jerome, *In Epistolam Pauli ad Galatas* (f) : s. viii^2, prob. England.

—   s.n.   [see no. **821**]

Göteborg, Friherre August Vilhelm Stiernstedts Samling

—   no. 3   [see no. **936.1**]

—   no. 4   [see no. **936**]

Gotha, Landesbibliothek

829.5   Mbr. I.18   Gospels : s. viii, Northumbria or Continent, prov. Murbach.

Grand Haven, Michigan, The Scriptorium

829.8   VK 861   Verse riddles ; Eugenius of Toledo (?), *Heptametron de primordio mundi* (SK 12551) ; Note on the languages of the world ; Note on loan of books (s. xi/xii) ; Responsory (s. xi/xii) : s. x/xi, Canterbury CC?, prov. N France s. xi (doubtful). [A flyleaf].

Haarlem, Stadsbibliotheek

—   188 F 53   [see no. **141**]

The Hague, Koninklijke Bibliotheek

830   133.D.22 (21)   Ælfric, *Catholic Homilies** (f ; from I.xxvii-xxix) : s. xi^1 [prob. from the same MS as nos. **811.5** and **816.5**].

Hamburg, Staats- und Universitätsbibliothek

830.5 cod. theol.   Gospels (f) : s. viii, prob. England [lost or destroyed?].
         2029 8°, flyleaf

Hannover, Kestner-Museum

831   W.M.XXIa, 36   Gospels, Gospel list : c. 1020, Canterbury CC, prov. Germany by s. xi, (prov. Lüneburg, Abbey of St. Michael).

126

831.2 Cul.I.71/72   [with New Haven, Yale University, Beinecke Library, 441]
(393/394)   Beda, *In Evangelium Lucae* (f) : s. viii/ix, England or Germany.

Hauzenstein near Regensburg, Gräflich Walderdorffsche Bibliothek

—   s.n.   [see no. **791**]

Herrnstein near Siegburg, Bibliothek der Grafen Nesselrode (formerly at Herten)

831.4 192, fols.   Antonius Musa, *De herba vettonica* ; Pseudo-Apuleius, *Herbarius* ;
1-20   *De taxone liber* ; Sextus Placitus, *Liber medicinae ex animalibus* :
s. ix^2 or ix/x, prob. S England (or NW Germany?) [destroyed].

Jönköping, Per Brahe gymnasiet

—   Fragm. 5 and 6   [see no. **936**]

Karlsruhe, Badische Landesbibliothek

—   Aug. perg. 116   [see no. **831.7**]
(binding)

831.6 Aug. perg. 221,   Gregory, *Homiliae in Ezechielem* : s. viii med., prob. Northumbria.
fols. 54-107

831.7 Fragm.Aug.122   [with Aug.perg. 116 (binding) and Zürich, Staatsarchiv A.G.19,
Nr.XIII, fols. 26-27]
Priscian, *Institutio de nomine, pronomine et verbo* (f) : s. viii ex.,
prob. Northumbria.

831.8 Fragm.Aug.212   Priscian, *Periegesis* (f) : s. x in. or x^1, England, or France?

Kassel, Gesamthochschulbibliothek

832 2°Ms.theol.21   Jerome, *In Ecclesiasten* ; Ambrose, *De apologia prophetae David* ;
Jerome, *Altercatio Luciferani et orthodoxi*, *Epistola* 57 : s. viii,
Northumbria, prov. Fulda s. ix?

833 2°Ms.theol.32   Gregory, *Regula pastoralis* : s. viii, S England, prov. Germany,
prob. Fulda, s. viii/ix.

834 2°Ms.theol.65   Josephus, *De bello Judaico* (version by 'Hegesippus'): s. vi, Italy,
prov. England s. viii, prov. Fulda s. viii?, (prov. ibid.).

—   2°Ms.theol.265   [see no. **849**]

835   4°Ms.theol.2   Beda, *Historia ecclesiastica*, bks. iv and v : s. viii^2, Northumbria, prov. Fulda prob. s. ix.

—   4°Ms.theol.131   [see no. **375**]

Köln (Cologne), Dombibliothek

836   213   Collection of Canons (*Collectio Sanblasiana*) : s. viii in., Northumbria, prov. Köln by s. viii ex.

Köln, Historisches Archiv der Stadt

836.5   GB Kasten B,   Sacramentarium Gelasianum (f) : s. viii med., prob. Northumbria.
nos. 24, 123, 124

Lawrence, University of Kansas, Kenneth Spencer Research Library

—   Pryce C2 :1   [see no. **117**]

—   Pryce C2 :2   [see no. **639**]

—   Pryce P2A :1   [see no. **436**]

Le Havre, Bibliothèque Municipale

837   330   Missal (incomplete) : s. xi$^{3/4}$ or xi^2 (or xi^1?), Winchester NM, (prov. Saint-Wandrille before s. xviii?).
FC : *The Missal of the New Minster, Winchester*, ed. D. H. Turner, HBS 93 (1962).

Leiden, Bibliotheek der Rijksuniversiteit

838   Voss.Lat.F.4,   Pliny, *Naturalis historia*, bks. ii-vi (incomplete) : s. viii$^{1/3}$,
fols. 4-33   Northumbria.

—   Voss.Lat.Q.2,   [see no. **795**]
fol. 60

839   Scaliger 69   Aethicus Ister, *Cosmographia* : s. x^2, Canterbury StA, prov. Glastonbury?

Leipzig, Universitätsbibliothek

840 Rep.I.58a and Gospels (f) : s. viii[1], Northumbria?
  II.35a

St. Petersburg (Leningrad), Russian National Library

840.5 F.v.I.3, Job, with interlinear gloss from Philippus Presbyter, *Commentarii*,
  fols. 1-38 and Gregory, *Moralia* : s. viii[2], prob. Northumbria, (prov. Corbie).

840.6 F.v.I.3, Jerome, *In Isaiam* (abbreviated ; incomplete) : s. viii[2], prob.
  fols. 39-108 Northumbria, (prov. Corbie).

841 F.v.I.8 Gospels : s. viii ex. or ix in., Northumbria? S England (Kent)?,
    (prov. Saint-Maur-les-Fosses).

842 O.v.I.1, fols. [with Avranches, Bibliothèque Municipale, 48, fols. i and ii ;
  1 and 2 66, fols. i and ii ; 71, fols. A and B]
    Gospels (f) : s. viii[1], Northumbria, (prov. Mont Saint-Michel).

842.5 O.v.I.45 Psalter and prayers : s. xi/xii, England [Returned to Poland before
    1928, but lost or destroyed (in Kraków or Warsaw). Formerly listed
    as no. **943**].

843 O.v.XIV.1 Frithegod, *Breviloquium Vitae Wilfridi* (incomplete : chs. i-xlvii) :
    s. x med., prob. Canterbury CC.

844 O.v.XVI.1, Priscian, *Institutio de nomine, pronomine et verbo* ; *Passio SS.*
  fols. 1-16 *Dionysii, Rustici et Eleutherii* (f ; *BHL* 2171) ; Maxim* ; On Gregory
    the Great (f) : s. x in. or x[1] ; Hymn, Two prayers ; Three sequences
    (W 20298 ; SK 9879, 17050) : added s. xi on Continent?

845 Q.v.I.15 Isidore, *Prooemia Veteris et Novi Testamenti, De ortu et obitu*
    patrum ; Jerome, *Epistola* 53 ; Isidore, *De ecclesiasticis officiis* ;
    Solutions to Aldhelm's *Aenigmata* ; Isidore, *Differentiae*, bk.ii ;
    Quicumque vult ; Acrostic poem (SK 8331 ; by Bonifatius?) ; Isidore,
    Synonyma I-II.33 (part of *Synonyma* continued at Corbie s. viii) ;
    Poems on the zodiac and the winds (SK 1037, 13113) ; Aldhelm,
    Aenigmata : s. viii[2], SW England, prov. Corbie s. viii.

846 Q.v.I.18 Beda, *Historia ecclesiastica* : 731×746, Wearmouth-J.

847 Q.v.XIV.1 Paulinus of Nola, *Carmina natalitia* 15, 16, 18, 28, 27, 17 : s. viii[1],
    Northumbria (Lindisfarne?), (prov. Corbie).

Leuven (Louvain), Katholieke Universiteit, Centrale Bibliotheek

847.5   s.n.   Psalterium Gallicanum (f) : s. x med.

Louvain-la-Neuve, Archives de l'Université Catholique de Louvain

848   Fragmenta   recto : Eleven medical recipes* (f) : s. ix ex. or x in.
       H. Omont 3   verso : Service book? (f) : s. vii/viii, Italy?

Lund, Universitetsbiblioteket

—   Fragm.membr.   [see no. **936**]
      lat. 1

Luzern, Staatsarchiv

848.4   Fragm.   Isidore, *Sententiae* (f) : s. viii^2, Northumbria.
       PA 1034/21007

Maaseik, Église Sainte-Catherine, Trésor

848.6   s.n., fols. 1-5   Gospels (f : Canon tables) : s. viii in., Northumbria, or Echternach.

848.7   s.n., fols. 6-132   Gospels : s. viii^1, Northumbria, or Echternach.

Malibu, now Los Angeles, California, J. Paul Getty Museum

848.8   9   Gospels (f) : s. x/xi or xi in., Canterbury? [Formerly listed as no. **817**].

Marburg, Hessisches Staatsarchiv

849   Hr 2, 17   [with Kassel, Gesamthochschulbibliothek 2°Ms.theol.265]
                         Jerome, *In Danielem* (f) : s. viii.

849.3   Hr 2, 18   Bonifatius, *Ars grammatica* (f) : s. viii med., S England [formerly
                         Oberkaufungen, Archiv des Ritterschaftlichen Stifts Kaufungen].

849.6   319 Pfarrei   Servius, *In Aeneida* (f) : s. viii^1, SW England, prov. s. viii prob. Fulda
       Spangenberg   [Formerly listed as no. **935**].
       Hr Nr. 1

Miskolc, Lévay József Library

850 s.n. Aldhelm, *Aenigmata* (f), *Epistola ad Acircium* (f) : s. viii, S England.

Monte Cassino, Archivio della Badia

851 BB. 437 Gospels : s. xi med. (c. 1065?) England, prov. Bavaria c. 1071, prov.
and 439 Italy c. 1089.

München, Bayerische Staatsbibliothek

[Shelfmarks of nos. **852-855** have been changed]

851.6 clm 14096, Isidore, *Prooemia Veteris et Novi Testamenti, De ortu et obitu*
fols. 1-99 *patrum, Allegoriae sacrae Scripturae* ; Florilegium from the Bible
and the Fathers (by Eligius of Noyon?) : s. viii/ix, Wales or Cornwall
or Brittany, (prov. Regensburg, St. Emmeram).

852 clm 29336(1 Prudentius, *Psychomachia*, with glosses (f) : s. x ex. or xi in.,
(prov. Germany s. xv) [formerly clm 29031b].

853 clm 29270(9 Gospels (f) : s. viii in., Northumbria? [formerly clm 29155d].

854 clm 29270(2 Gospels (f) : s. vii ex. [formerly clm 29155e].

855 clm 29698(2 'Petrocellus' (f) : s. xi?, England? [formerly clm 29137b].

München, Hauptstaatsarchiv

855.5 Raritäten-Selekt Calendar (f) : s. viii^2, Northumbria (or Continent?), prov. Tegernsee
108 or Ilmmünster s. ix [lost].

München, Stadtarchiv

— Historischer [see no. **791.9**]
Verein
Oberbayern Hs. 733/16

131

Münster in Westfalen, Staatsarchiv

856   MSC.I.243,   [with Braunschweig, Stadtbibliothek, Fragm.70 and Bückeburg,
        fols. 1, 2,   Niedersächsisches Staatsarchiv, Depot 3/1]
        11 and 12   Beda, *De temporum ratione* (f) ; Dionysius Exiguus, *Cyclus Paschalis* : s. viii[1], Northumbria?

Münster in Westfalen, Universitätsbibliothek

856.1   Fragmenten-   Gregory, *Dialogi* (f) : s. viii[2].
         kapsel 1 no. 2

856.2   Fragmenten-   Beda, *Historia ecclesiastica* (f) : s. viii[2].
         kapsel 1 no. 3

856.3   Fragmenten-   Sacramentary (Gelasianum mixtum ; f) : s. viii[1], Northumbria,
         sammlung IV.8   (prov. Werden).

New Haven, Yale University, Beinecke Library

—   320   [see no. **157**]

857   401   [with 401A ; Cambridge, University Library, Add. 3330 ; London, B.L. Add. 50483 K and 71687 ; Oslo and London, The Schøyen Collection, 197 ; Oxford, Bodleian Library, Arch.A.f.131 (ptd. bk.) and lat.th.d.24, fols. 1 and 2 ; Philadelphia, Free Library, John Frederick Lewis Collection, ET 121]
Aldhelm, *De virginitate* (prose)° : s. ix in. (or viii ex.?), OE glosses s. x[2].

—   401A   [see no. **857**]

—   441   [see no. **831.2**]

858   516   Gregory, *Moralia* (f) : s. viii[1], Northumbria.

859   578   Gospels* (f) : s. x/xi or xi[1], SE England?, (prov. prob. SW England, Tewkesbury?).

—   Osborn fa 26   [see no. **146**]

New York, Pierpont Morgan Library

860   M 708   Gospels : s. xi med. (c. 1065?), England, prov. Bavaria c. 1071, prov. Weingarten s. xi ex.

861	M 709	Gospels : s. xi med. (c. 1065?), England, prov. Bavaria c. 1071, prov. Weingarten s. xi ex.
862	M 776	Psalterium Romanum, with glosses (incomplete) : s. viii med., prov. S England? OE and Latin glosses s. ix (Wessex) and x^2, (prov. City of Lincoln).
863	M 826	Beda, *Historia ecclesiastica* (f) : s. viii ex., Northumbria, prov. Bath? and (s. xi^2) Saint-Vaast, Arras?
863.5	M 827	Gospels : s. x^2, NE France, prov. England s. x/xi or xi^1?
864	M 869	Gospels : s. x ex., prob. Canterbury CC, (prov. Köln, St. Severin, by s. xii, or s. xi?).
865	M 926, fols. 1-41	Leontius (trans. Anastasius Bibliothecarius), *Vita Johannis Eleemosynarii* : s. xi/xii, Continent, (prov. St. Albans), in England by 1100?
865.1	M 926, fols. 42-52	Three Hymns to St. Alban (including *AH* 11.67, 11.68), Office and Mass of St. Alban : s. $xi^{3/4}$, St. Albans.
865.2	M 926, fols. 53-68	Hymn to St. Dunstan (SK 7449) ; Adelard, *Vita S. Dunstani* : s. $xi^{3/4}$, (prov. St. Albans).
865.3	M 926, fols. 70-73	*Vita S. Alexii* (*BHL* 286) : s. xi/xii, (prov. St. Albans).
865.4	M 926, fols. 74-78	Versicles, antiphons, responds for feast of St. Birinus ; Odo of Cluny, Sermon for feast of St. Benedict ; Fragment of sermon (parts of Augustine, *De ordine*) : s. $xi^{3/4}$, (prov. St. Albans).
865.5	G 30	Gregory, *Moralia* (f) : s. vii ex., prob. Northumbria.
866	G 63	Hexateuch* (f : from Exodus) : s. xi^2.

New York, Public Library

866.5	115	Gospels, Gospel list : s. $ix^{3/3}$, Landévennec (Brittany), prov. SW England s. x med., (prov. s. xviii Italy).

Orléans, Bibliothèque Municipale

867	127 (105)	Sacramentary : s. $x^{3/4}$, Winchcombe? or s. $x^{4/4}$, Ramsey?, prov. Fleury s. xi in. FC : *The Winchcombe Sacramentary*, ed. A. Davril, HBS 109 (1995).

868	342 (290), pp. 1-68	[palimpsest, lower script] Unidentified text : s. viii.
869	342 (290)	Six lives of saints and miracles (*BHL* 6104-6106, 286, 730, 4171, 412, 8024) ; Six sermons ; Pseudo-Jerome, *Epistolae supp.* 48 and 49 : s. x/xi, England or Fleury?, (prov. Fleury).

Oslo, Riksarkivet

Lat.fragm. :

870	201	[with Oslo, Universitetsbiblioteket Lat.fragm. 9] Mass lectionary (f) : s. $x^{1/4}$.
871	204, 1-4, 9 and 10	[with Copenhagen, Rigsarkivet M.H.4593] Missal (f) : s. xi med.
—	204, 5-6 and 205, 1-2	[see no. **936**]
871.5	206, 209, 1-4 and 239, 6-7	Missal (f) : s. xi in., Winchester.
872	207, 208 and 210	[with Copenhagen, Rigsarkivet, M.H.3084 and 3085] Missal (f) : s. x/xi, Winchester?, (prov. diocese of Oslo).
—	208	[see no. **872**]
—	209, 1-4	[see no. **871.5**]
—	210	[see no. **872**]
872.5	211	Mass lectionary (f) : s. x or xi, England?
873	223, 1 and 2	Antiphoner (f) : s. xi ex.
873.5	225, 1 and 2	Antiphoner (f) : s. xi/xii, England or Norway.
874	226, 1 and 2	Antiphoner (f) : s. xi ex.
874.3	226, 3-9	Gradual (f) : s. xi.
874.6	227, 1-23	Missal (f) : s. xi^1.
875	228, 1-21	Missal (f) : s. xi^2.
—	239, 6-7	[see no. **871.5**]

Oslo, Universitetsbiblioteket

—   Lat.fragm. 9   [see no. **870**]

875.2   Lat.fragm. 16   Pontifical (f) : s. xi.

Oslo and London, The Schøyen Collection

875.4   76   Beda, *De tabernaculo* : s. xi/xii, England or Continent.

—   79   [see no. **677.3**]

—   197   [see no. **857**]

875.5   674   Missal (f) : s. xi med.

875.6   1542   Missal (f) : s. xi^1.

875.7   2366   Augustine, *Enchiridion* (f) : s. xi med.

Paris, Bibliothèque de l'Arsenal

—   903, fols. 1-52   [see no. **903**]

Paris, Bibliothèque Nationale

876   anglais 67   Ælfric, *Grammar*+* (f) : s. xi^1.

876.5 français 2452,   Psalterium Hebraicum (f) : s. ix^1, Wales or SW England.
          fols. 75-84

877   lat. 272   Gospel list, Gospels : s. x^2 or x ex. or x/xi, Winchester?,
                            (prov. prob. Normandy – Fécamp? – s. xi or later).

878   lat. 281 and 298   Gospels : s. viii ex., S England, perh. Canterbury (or Mercia?),
                            (prov. Fécamp s. xi or later).

879   lat. 943   Letter from Pope John XII to Dunstan ; Pontifical ; Benedictional ;
                            Prologue to *Poenitentiale Egberti* ; First Capitulary of Gerbald of
                            Liège ; Forms of absolution : s. x$^{3/4}$ (after 959), prob. Canterbury CC.
                            Additions : List of bishops of Sherborne ; Letter to Bishop Wulsige III
                            of Sherborne ; Two homilies for the Dedication of a church* (one by
                            Ælfric) ; Rules of confraternity* and Formula-letter announcing the
                            death of a monk ; Part of Mass of the Dead ; Two penitential letters ;
                            Writ by Bishop Æthelric of Sherborne* : s. x/xi - xi^1, Sherborne.

Prov. whole MS Sherborne by s. x/xi, France s. xi².
FC : Prescott (1987), pp. 141-147, for benedictions.

880	lat. 987	Benedictional : fols. 1-84 s. x²ᐟ³, Winchester OM ; fols. 85-111 s. xi²ᐟ⁴ or xi³ᐟ⁴, Canterbury CC, (prov. France before late s. xvi?).

880 lat. 987 Benedictional : fols. 1-84 s. $x^{2/3}$, Winchester OM ; fols. 85-111 s. $xi^{2/4}$ or $xi^{3/4}$, Canterbury CC, (prov. France before late s. xvi?).

881 lat. 1751 Ambrose, *De virginibus, De viduis, De virginitate, Exhortatio virginitatis* ; Nicetas of Remesiana (?), *De lapsu virginis consecratae* ; Ambrose, *De mysteriis* ; (Pseudo?-)Ambrose, *De sacramentis* ; Pseudo-Jerome, *Epistola* 38 ('*Homilia de corpore et sanguine Christi*') : s. xi² or xi ex., Canterbury StA?

881.7 lat. 2621, fols. 84-92 Hermannus Archidiaconus (attrib.), *Miracula S. Eadmundi* (short version) : s. xi/xii, England or Normandy.

882 lat. 2825, fols. 57-81 Beda, *Vita S. Cuthberti* (verse), with Latin and OE glosses (s. x) ; Grammatical examples ; Notes on the Ages of the World, the Ages of Man, the human body, on the dimensions of the world, of the Temple of Solomon, of Noah's Ark, on the books of the Bible, on measures of length : s. ix/x, NE France, prov. England by s. x med.

883 lat. 4210 Smaragdus, *Expositio in Regulam S. Benedicti* : s. x/xi, prov. Fécamp.

884 lat. 4839 Priscian, *Periegesis* ; Nemesianus, *Cynegetica* ; Q. Serenus, *Liber medicinalis* : s. x/xi, England.

885 lat. 4871, fols. 161-168 Isidore, *Etymologiae* (f) : s. viii/ix, Northumbria?

885.3 lat. 5362, fols. 1-84 Beda, *Vita S. Cuthberti* (prose) ; Excerpts from Beda, *Historia ecclesiastica* (on lives of St. Cuthbert, St. Oswald, St. Birinus, St. Æthelthryth) ; Excerpt from *Historia de S. Cuthberto* ; Abbo of Fleury, *Vita S. Eadmundi* ; Lantfred, *Translatio et miracula S. Swithuni* (abbrev.) ; Ælfric, *Vita S. Æthelwoldi* : s. xi/xii, England (or Normandy?), (prov. Fécamp).

885.5 lat. 5574, fols. 1-39 *Passio S. Christophori* (*BHL* 1768-1770) ; *Inventio s. Crucis* (*BHL* 4169) ; *Exaltatio s. Crucis* (partly *BHL* 4178) ; *Passiones S. Margaretae* (*BHL* 5303), *S. Julianae* (incomplete ; *BHL* 4522) : s. ix/x or x¹ᐟ⁴, (prov. France s. xii).

885.6 lat. 5575, fols. 1-41 *Passio et miracula S. Quintini* (*BHL* 7005, 7006, 7018) : s. x².

886 lat. 6401 Radulf of Liège and Ragimbold of Cologne, Letters on geometry (s. xi) ; Boethius, *De consolatione Philosophiae, De institutione arithmetica* ; Epitaphium Gauzlini (s. xi ; SK 12433) : s. x/xi, England or Fleury?, prov. Fleury s. xi.

887	lat. 6401A	Boethius, *De consolatione Philosophiae*, with glosses and commentary by Remigius (redaction BN) : s. x ex. or x/xi, Canterbury CC, prov. France (Saint-Vaast, Arras?) s. xi (or later?).
888	lat. 7299, fols. 3-12	Calendar ; Computus materials : s. x/xi, Ramsey?, prov. Fleury.
889	lat. 7585	Isidore, *Etymologiae* (s. ix$^{2/4}$ or ix^2 France, and x^2 England) ; Treatise on the Trinity (s. x^2) ; Ælfric, *De falsis diis** (excerpt, s. xi^1): s. ix$^{2/4}$ or ix^2, NE France, in England (prob. Canterbury StA) by s. x^2.
889.5	lat. 8085, fols. 2-82	Prudentius, *Cathemerinon, Peristephanon, Apotheosis, Hamartigenia, Psychomachia, Contra Symmachum, Dittochaeon* : s. ix$^{2/3}$ or ix med., France, prob. Loire region, prov. England prob. by s. x/xi.
890	lat. 8092	Sedulius, Letter I to Macedonius, *Carmen Paschale* with glosses (some OE), Hymns ; Poems on Sedulius (SK 14842, 14841) ; Pseudo-Columbanus, *Praecepta vivendi* ; Beda, *De die iudicii* ; Arator, *Historia apostolica*, with glosses ; Three Latin poems (including SK 15583) : s. xi$^{2/4}$, England, prov. France (s. xi^2?).
890.5	lat. 8431, fols. 21-48	Frithegod, *Breviloquium Vitae Wilfridi*, with commentary : 948×958, Canterbury CC?, prov. France (s. x^2?).
891	lat. 8824	Psalterium Romanum^{+*}, with (Ps 1-50) OE prose translation by King Alfred and (Ps 51-150) OE metrical version ; Canticles ; Litany ; Prayers : s. xi med., (prov. France by s. xiv).
892	lat. 9377, fol. 3	Epistola Pauli ad Corinthios II (f) : s. viii^1, Northumbria?, prov. France (s. viii?).
893	lat. 9389	Gospels : s. vii/viii, Northumbria, prob. Lindisfarne (Ireland? Echternach?), prov. Echternach.
893.5	lat. 9488, fols. 3-4	Sacramentary (Gelasianum mixtum ; f) : s. viii, prob. Northumbria.
893.8	lat. 9555, fol. 1	[Palimpsest, lower script] Patristic fragment : s. viii, prob. England.
894	lat. 9561	Pseudo-Isidore, *De ordine creaturarum* ; Gregory, *Regula pastoralis* : s. viii^1 or viii med., S England, (prov. Saint-Bertin by s. xiv or xv).
895	lat. 10062, fols. 162-163	Calendar (f) : s. xi in., Canterbury CC, (prov. Saint-Évroult).

896	lat. 10575	Prologue to *Poenitentiale Egberti* ; First Capitulary of Gerbald of Liège ; Pontifical ; Benedictional : s. x med. or x² or x/xi, prov. Évreux s. xi. FC : Banting (1989), pp. 1-153.
897	lat. 10837, fols. 34-41 and 44	Calendar ; Easter tables : s. viii in., England? Echternach?, prov. Echternach.
898	lat. 10861	Nineteen Lives of saints ; Sayings and riddles (add. s. ix² or x) : s. ix^{1/4} or ix¹, S England (Canterbury CC?), prov. France s. x or xi, (prov. Beauvais s. xiii). FC : M. P. Brown, *ASE* 15 (1986), 122.
898.5	lat. 13089, fols. 49-76	Gregory, *Regula pastoralis*, iii.9-29 : s. viii med. or viii², Northumbria (Wearmouth-J.?).
899	lat. 14380, fols. 1-65	Boethius, *De consolatione Philosophiae*, with *accessus*, and commentary by Remigius : s. x ex., Canterbury CC, (prov. Paris, Saint-Victor, Augustinian canons).
900	lat. 14782	Gospels : s. xi² or xi ex., Exeter, (prov. Paris, Saint-Victor).
900.5	lat. 17177, fols. 5-12	[with Rome, Biblioteca Apostolica Vaticana, lat. 304, flyleaf] Theodore of Mopsuestia, *Commentarii in Epistolas Pauli* (in Latin ; f) : s. viii¹ or viii/ix, S England or Mercia, or Continent?
901	lat. 17814	Boethius, *De consolatione Philosophiae*, with *accessus*, and commentary by Remigius : s. x ex., prob. Canterbury CC.
902	nouv.acq. lat. 586, fols. 16-131	*Excerptiones de Prisciano* ; Excerpt from Beda, *De temporum ratione*, ch. iv : s. x² or xi¹.

Paris, Bibliothèque Sainte-Geneviève

903	2410	[with Paris, Bibliothèque de l'Arsenal MS 903, fols. 1-52] Juvencus, *Libri Evangeliorum* ; Commentary on the Gospel of St. Matthew (incomplete ; unidentified) ; Greek litany and Sanctus ; Eugenius of Toledo (?), *Heptametron de primordio mundi* (SK 12551) ; Israel the Grammarian, *De arte metrica* (SK 14932) ; *Rubisca* (SK 11608) ; Metrical versions of Pater noster and Credo (SK 10905 ; 15347 [from Juvencus i.589-603] ; 2593) ; Greek numbers in Latin letters ; Poem 'De quattuor clavibus sapientiae' ; Two distichs from Ovid (*Amores* 3.8.3-4, SK 8093 ; *Ars amat.* 2.279-80, SK 8353) ; Verses by Alcuin (from *carm.* 80.1; SK 11084) ; Sedulius, Letter I to Macedonius, *Carmen paschale*, Hymn (SK 33) ; Poems on Sedulius (SK 14842, 14841) ; Excerpt from Aldhelm,

Epistola ad Acircium ; Odo of Cluny, *Occupatio* : s. x ex. - xi in., prob. Canterbury CC (or StA?).

Philadelphia, Free Library, John Frederick Lewis Collection

—   ET 121   [see no. **857**]

Prague, Národní Knihovna Ceské Republiky

904   Roudnice   Gospels (f) : s. viii^1, Northumbria.
         VI.Fe.50

Princeton, Princeton University Library, W. H. Scheide Collection

905   71   Homilies* ('Blickling Homilies') : s. x/xi.

Regensburg, Bischöfliche Zentralbibliothek

—   Cim. 1   [see no. **791**]

Rheims, Bibliothèque Municipale

906   9   Gospels : s. xi med., prov. 1062×1065 Saint-Remi, Rheims.

906.5   1097   Priscian, *Partitiones xii versuum Aeneidos principalium* : s. x^2 ;
                Anglo-Saxon regnal list : s. xi/xii, (prov. France s. xii).

Rome, Vatican City, Biblioteca Apostolica Vaticana

907   Barberini   Gospels : s. viii^2 or viii ex. or ix in., Mercia or Northumbria?
         lat. 570   Canterbury?

—   lat. 304, flyleaf   [see no. **900.5**]

907.5   lat. 3228   Cicero, *Philippicae* : s. x^2, England?

908   lat. 3363   Boethius, *De consolatione Philosophiae*, with glosses (s. ix ex.
                and x) ; Glossary to Prudentius, *Psychomachia* : s. ix^1, Loire region
                (Orléans? Fleury?), prov. Wales or Cornwall or SW England s. ix ex.,
                prov. England (Glastonbury?) by s. x med.

909	Pal.lat. 68, fols. 1-46	Catena on the Psalms (incomplete, only Ps 39-151) : s. viii, Northumbria, prov. Lorsch or Mainz by s. ix?
910	Pal.lat. 235, fols. 4-29	Paulinus of Nola, *Carmina natalitia* 15, 16, 18, 28, 27, 17 : s. viii in., Northumbria (Lindisfarne? Wearmouth-J.?), prov. s. viii Germany (Lorsch? Fulda?).
911	Pal.lat. 259	Gregory, *Homiliae in Ezechielem* : s. viii-ix, England or Continent?
911.5	Pal.lat. 554, fols. 5-13	*Poenitentiale Egberti*, Prologue and chs. i-xiii : s. viii/ix, England or Continent (Lorsch?), prov. s. ix[1] Lorsch.
912	Reg.lat. 12	Calendar ; Computus material ; Psalterium Gallicanum ; Canticles ; Litany ; Prayers : s. xi[2/4], prob. Canterbury CC, prov. Bury St. Edmunds, (prov. Jouarre s. xii).
913	Reg.lat. 204	Office of St. Cuthbert (f) ; Beda, *Vita S. Cuthberti* (verse), with glosses ; Note on the Six Ages of Man : s. xi in., Canterbury StA (CC?), (prov. Bonneval by s. xiv).
914	Reg.lat. 338, fols. 64-126	'Metrical calendar of York' (incomplete) ; Amalarius (?), *Eclogae de ordine Romano* ; Caesarius, *De decem plagis et praeceptis* (*Sermo* 100) ; Horologium ; Alphabets (including two runic alphab.) ; Two pontifical ordines ; Benedictional ; Pseudo-Jerome, *Breviarium in psalmos* ; Hymnal : s. x^2 or x/xi, N France or Germany ; Charm* ; Prayer : s. xi[1] ; all prov. England s. xi[1]??
915	Reg.lat. 489, fols. 61-124	('Martinellus') : Sulpicius Severus, *Vita S. Martini*, *Epistolae*, *Dialogi* ; Gregory of Tours, Extracts from *Historia Francorum* and *De virtutibus S. Martini* ; *Vita S. Bricii* (from *Historia Francorum* ii.1) : s. xi[1] or earlier.
916	Reg.lat. 497, fol. 71	Orosius, *Historiae adversus paganos** (f) : s. xi.
917	Reg.lat. 946, fols. 72-76	Decree (Laws : *Æthelred X*)* (prob. from a service-book) : s. xi[1], (prov. Normandy, prob. Avranches, in or before s. xii).
918	Reg.lat. 1283, fol. 114	Grammatical note ; Excerpts from St. Augustine : s. x^2 ; Excerpts from Ælfric, *De temporibus anni* * : s. xi[1].
919	Reg.lat. 1671	Vergil, *Bucolica*, *Georgica*, *Aeneid*, all with glosses (s. xi), partly from Servius, and (*Georgica*, *Aeneid*) with *argumenta* by Pseudo-Ovid ; Excerpts from Pseudo-Vergil, *Culex*, and Ovid, *Metamorphoses* (xiii.100) ; Five Latin poems (SK 12542 ; 10279 and 16845 [Pseudo-Vergil] ; 7221, 638) : s. x^2 or x/xi or xi[1/4], Worcester.

Rouen, Bibliothèque Municipale

919.3   26 (A.292)   Proverbia Salomonis, Ecclesiastes, Canticum canticorum ; Commentary on Canticum canticorum (excerpted from Alcuin's commentary) ; Alcuin, *carm.* 78 (SK 7355) ; Proverbs, poem (W 4803) ; Sapientia Salomonis ; Augustine, *Enchiridion* ; Isidore, *Etymologiae* XI, i-ii ; Tract on the Office ; Tract on the temperaments ; Responsio IX of Gregory to Augustine ; *Expositio missae* ('Primum in ordine') ; Computistical, astronomical and other scientific treatises including excerpt from Isidore, *De natura rerum*, and a tract on the winds ; Ordo Romanus XIII A ; Mass prayers, Office antiphons and responsories : s. ix[1] or ix med. ; N France.
fol. 48 : added drawing (s. x, England?), and verses from Hrabanus Maurus, *De laudibus s. crucis* (s. x[2]), and poem (W 4803, s. xi/xii). Whole MS prov. England s. x?, prov. Jumièges s. xi?

919.6   32 (A.21)   Gospels (incomplete) : 1087×1097, Abingdon, (prov. Jumièges).

920   231 (A.44)   Psalterium Gallicanum (incomplete) ; Canticles ; Litany ; Prayers ; Hymnal ; Monastic canticles : s. xi ex., Canterbury StA?, (prov. Jumièges).

921   274 (Y.6)   Calendar ; Computus material ; Sacramentary : 1014×1023, prov. (and origin?) Peterborough or Ely, prov. Canterbury CC?, prov. Jumièges s. xi med.
FC : *The Missal of Robert of Jumièges*, ed. H. A. Wilson, HBS 11 (1896).

922   368 (A.27)   Pontifical and Benedictional, including Prologue to *Poenitentiale Egberti*, and Gerbald of Liège, First Capitulary : s. xi in. or xi[1], SW England (St. Germans?), prov. Crediton by 1027×1046 (or Wells before 1014?), (prov. Jumièges).
FC : *Pontificale Lanalatense*, ed. G. H. Doble, HBS 74 (1937).

923   369 (Y.7)   Pontifical ; Benedictional : s. x[4/4] (s. xi[2/4]?) Winchester NM, (prov. Rouen cathedral from s. xii[1]).
FC : *The Benedictional of Archbishop Robert*, ed. H. A. Wilson, HBS 24 (1903).

924   506 (A.337)   Gregory, *Dialogi* (part) : s. x ex., Canterbury CC?

925   1382 (U.109), fols. 173-198   (A version of Wulfstan's 'Handbook') : Ordo Romanus XIIIA ; '*Institutio beati Amalarii*' (excerpts from *Liber officialis*) ; Sermon *De ieiunio quattuor temporum* ; *De ecclesiastica consuetudine* (excerpts from Amalarius, *Liber officialis*, and *Regularis Concordia*) ; Wulfstan's Canon Law Collection ('*Excerptiones Pseudo-Egberti*', recension A) ; Excerpts from *Admonitio generalis*, and *Institutio canonicorum* (of Aachen Council of 816) ; Prologue to *Poenitentiale*

141

Egberti ; First Capitulary of Gerbald of Liège : s. xi[1].
FC : Cross and Hamer (1999), pp. 40-41.

925.5	1384 (U.26), fols. 1-4	*Vita S. Judoci* (*BHL* 4504 ; by Alcuin?) : s. x$^{4/4}$, England or Jumièges?
926	1385 (U.107), fols. 20-26	*Memoriale qualiter* (incomplete) ; Acta praeliminaria of Council of Aachen 816 : s. x/xi, England? (Winchester or Worcester?), (prov. Jumièges).
927	1385 (U.107), fols. 28-85	Lantfred, *Translatio et miracula S. Swithuni* ; Wulfstan of Winchester, Four poems on Winchester saints : Swithun (2), Birinus, Æthelwold (SK 1530, 474, 1443, 591) ; Hymn (SK 11045) ; metrical version of Hymnus trium puerorum : s. x ex., Winchester OM, (prov. Jumièges).

Rygnestad, Norway, private archives

—	Archives of Ketil Rygnestad, no.95, and of Knut Rygnestad, no.99	[see no. **777**]

St. Gallen, Kantonalsbibliothek, Vadianische Sammlung

928	337	Letter by Wulfric, abbot of St. Augustine's, to Abbo of Fleury ; *Vita S. Dunstani* by 'B' (*BHL* 2342) : 995×1004, Canterbury StA, prov. Fleury s. x/xi.

St. Gallen, Stiftsbibliothek

929	1394, pp. 95-98	Sacramentary (f) : s. viii in., Northumbria, or Ireland?

Saint-Lô, Archives de la Manche

930	1	Gospels : s. xi$^{3/4}$ or xi^{2}, (prov. Saint-Évroult, prob. s. xi ex.).

Saint-Omer, Bibliothèque Municipale

930.5	202	Gospel of Nicodemus ; *Passio S. Margaretae* (*BHL* 5303) ; *Vindicta Salvatoris* ; thirty-five Homilies from Paulus Diaconus, *Homiliarium* : s. ix^{2}, NE France, prov. England (Exeter?) by s. xi med., (prov. Saint-Bertin).

FC : *Two Old English Apocrypha and their Manuscript Source*, ed. J. E. Cross, CSASE 19 (1996), pp. 22-31.

931   257, fols. 1-7   Gospels (f) : s. viii[1], Northumbria.

932   279, fols. 1-2   Isidore, *Differentiae* (f) : s. viii, England?, (prov. Saint-Bertin).

St. Paul in Carinthia, Stiftsbibliothek

933   2[1] (25.2.16)   Three commentaries on Donatus : Pompeius, *Commentum artis Donati* (extracts), (Poem, SK 3536, add. s. viii[2/3]) ; Anonymus ad Cuimnanum, *Expossitio Latinitatis* ; Sergius, *Explanationes in Donatum* : s. viii[1], prov. c. 800 Murbach.

933.5   979 (29.4.9),   Sacramentary (f) : s. viii-ix.
             fol. 4

St. Petersburg, Russian National Library : see nos. **840.5-847**

San Marino, California, Henry E. Huntington Library

934   HM 62   Bible : s. xi[2], Canterbury CC?, prov. Rochester.

—   RB 99513   [see no. **818.5**]
     (PR 1188F)

Sondershausen, Schlossmuseum

—   Br 1   [see no. **141**]

[Spangenberg, Pfarrbibliothek]

[935]   see now no. **849.3**

Stockholm, Riksarkivet

936   Mi 1   [with Göteborg, Friherre August Vilhelm Stiernstedts Samling, no. 4 ; Jönköping, Per Brahe gymnasiet, Fragm. 5 and 6 ; Lund, Universitetsbiblioteket, Fragm.membr.lat.1 ; Oslo, Riksarkivet, Lat.fragm. 204, 5-6 and 205, 1-2 ; Växjö, Smålands Museet, Fragm. L 1505/15]

Missal (f) : s. x/xi or xi in., Winchester?, (prov. diocese of Skara, Sweden).

936.1 Mi 134 [with Göteborg, Friherre August Vilhelm Stiernstedts Samling, no. 3] Missal (f) : s. xi$^{2/4}$, SE England?

936.2 Fragm. 194 and 195 Augustine, Sermones (f) : s. xi ex., Normandy, prov. England.

936.4 Fragm. 2070 Missal (f) : s. xi^1 or xi med.

936.5 Fragm. 2427 Missal (f) : s. xi med.

936.7 Lösa Pergaments- omslag S.9 Pontifical (?) (f) : s. x/xi.

Stockholm, Kungliga Biblioteket

936.9 A.128 Gradual (f) : s. xi$^{3/4}$.

937 A.135 Gospels ; Donation inscription* (s. ix med.) : s. viii med., Kent (Minster-in-Thanet or Canterbury?), prov. Canterbury CC.

937.1 Isl.perg.8° no. 8 Missal (f) : s. x ex.

Stuttgart, Württembergische Landesbibliothek

937.3 Theol. et Philos. Qu 628 Gregory, *Dialogi* : s. vii/viii, Northumbria or Continent.

Tokyo, Collection of Professor Toshiyuki Takamiya

— 21 [see no. **646**]

— 45 [one fol. in a leaf collection. See no. **504.3**]

937.5 55 Augustine, *In Psalmos* (f) : s. xi/xii, Canterbury CC. [From Companion vol. to nos. **170-171**].

Urbana, University of Illinois Library

938 128 Sylloge of Latin inscriptions (Bishop Mildred's collection ; f : Sixteen poems and inscriptions, recorded in Index II, below) : s. x med., prob. Worcester, (prov. Malmesbury).

144

Utrecht, Universiteitsbibliotheek

939 32 (Script. Psalterium Gallicanum ; Canticles : s. ix^1 (c. 816×c.840), Hautvillers
eccl.484), or Rheims, prov. Canterbury CC by s. x ex. or xi in.
fols. 1-91

940 32 (Script. Gospels (f) : s. viii in., Wearmouth-J.
eccl.484),
fols. 94-105

Valenciennes, Bibliothèque Municipale

940.5 195 (187) Alcuin, *De fide sanctae et individuae Trinitatis* (with *Epistola* 289) ;
De Trinitate ad Fredegisum quaestiones XXVIII (with *Epistola* 309
and including *carm*. 85.1-3) : s. ix in., S England?, prov. s. ix/x
Saint-Amand.

Växjö, Smålands Museet

— Fragm. L 1505/15 [see no. **936**]

Vercelli, Biblioteca Capitolare

941 CXVII Homilies*, including part of the OE Life of St. Guthlac ; OE Poetry :
*Andreas** ; Cynewulf, *Fates of the Apostles* * ; *Soul and Body** ;
Homiletic verse fragment* ; *Dream of the Rood** ; Cynewulf, *Elene** :
s. x^2, SE England (Canterbury StA? Rochester?).

Warsaw, Biblioteka Narodowa

942 I.3311 Gospel lectionary and Gospel list (both incomplete) : s. x/xi.

[943] See now no. **842.5**.

Washington, D.C., Folger Shakespeare Library

943.2 ptd. bk. Unidentified text* (f) : s. xi.
(binding)

Weimar, Landesbibliothek

943.4 Fol. 414a Isidore, *De natura rerum* (f) : s. viii^2, prob. England.

Weinheim, olim Sammlung E. Fischer

—   s.n.   [Lost? See no. **176**]

—   s.n.   [Lost? See no. **441.1**]

Wrisbergholzen (near Alfeld/Leine), Archiv des Grafen von Goertz-Wrisberg

943.6   HS Nr. 3   Jerome, *Tractatus in Psalmos* (f ; from Ps 76 and 77) : s. ix$^{1/3}$, England or Germany.

Wroclaw (Breslau), Biblioteka Uniwersytecka

943.8   Akc. 1955/2   Gregory, *Dialogi* (f) : s. viii^1 or viii med., Northumbria.
        and 1969/430

Würzburg, Universitätsbibliothek

944   M.p.th.q.2   Jerome, *In Ecclesiasten* : s. v, Italy, prov. England s. vii, Worcester diocese c. 700, prov. Würzburg s. viii.

944.3   M.p.th.q.24   Isidore, *Quaestiones in Vetus Testamentum* : s. viii^2, England, or Germany?

944.5   M.p.th.f.43   Augustine, *In Psalmos* (excerpts) ; Gregory, *Homiliae in Ezechielem* I, 8 and 9 : s. viii med., prov. Würzburg.

944.8   M.p.th.f.62   Liturgical calendar of Rome ; Epistle list ; Gospel list : s. viii med., England or Italy (Rome)?, prov. Würzburg s. viii.

945   M.p.th.f.68   Gospels : s. vi, Italy, prov. Northumbria s. vii ex., or Germany (Mainz)?, prov. Würzburg s. viii.

946   M.p.th.f.79   Isidore, *Synonyma* (incomplete) : s. viii^1, S England or Mercia, prov. Germany, Rhine-Main area (Mainz?) s. viii ex., then Würzburg.

946.5   M.p.th.f.149a   Gregory, *Moralia*, bks. 32-35 : s. viii^2, S Mercia or Germany?

Zürich, Staatsarchiv des Kantons Zürich

—   A.G.19, no.XIII,   [see no. **831.7**]
        fols. 26 and 27

Zürich, Zentralbibliothek

947   Z XIV 30, Nr. 11   Eucherius, *Formulae* (f) : s. viii med.

III. UNTRACED

Formerly Mr H. Bailey of Salisbury : Gospels (f), s. xi[1].
Positive photostats at the Bodleian Library, Oxford : MS Facs.c.27, fols. 8a-b. From the same book as no. **645.5**?

For other lost or untraced manuscripts or fragments see nos. **176**, **441.1**, **643**, **842.5**, **855.5**, and N. R. Ker, *Catalogue of Manuscripts Containing Anglo-Saxon* (1957), nos. 403-412.

INDEXES

Index I
Authors and texts

All references are to the serial numbers of the *Handlist*.
The following symbols and abbreviations have been used :

*	text in Old English. Where the asterisk immediately follows the title of a work, all serial references are to the text in Old English
**	text in Old English alliterative verse
(*)	text partly in Old English
+*	text in Latin and Old English prose, or Latin-Old English glossary
°	Latin text with continuous Old English gloss, or with substantial sections, or a fairly large number of words, glossed in Old English
e	excerpts or parts of a text
f	fragment ; incompleteness of a text is noted in the *Handlist*, but not in this Index
(?)	Authorship doubtful

Names in round brackets are usually those of the translators of Greek or Latin works.
It is recommended that this Index should be used together with that in N. R. Ker's *Catalogue of Manuscripts Containing Anglo-Saxon*, pp. 517-50.

Advent Lyrics**, *see Christ I***

Ælfric, archbishop, Verses commemorating him 775

Ælfric Bata, Colloquies 686

Ælfric of Eynsham (Prefaces to his works are not separately listed)

    Admonitio (by Pseudo-Basil)* 632

    *Catholic Homilies** 11, 58, 352f, 363e, 403, 406, 428f, 442f, 472, 569, 670f, 811.5f, 816.6f, 828f, 830f

    Colloquy 363°, 686, 775

    *Creed** 322

    *De duodecim abusivis** 54, 639

    *De falsis diis** 339, 889e

    Glossary[+]** 13, 115, 331, 336, 414, 541e, 686

    Grammar[+]** 13, 115, 182, 244, 331, 336, 414, 435, 441f, 480f, 494, 541e, 686, 876f

    Hexateuch* (part trans. by Ælfric) 65.5e, 276f, 315, 657, 866f

    Homilies* and Sermons* 18, 50, 54, 59.5, 64, 86, 109, 122f, 146f, 177, 262f, 355, 359, 363, 435, 520, 637, 638, 639, 644, 879 ; (?) Sermon in Latin 800

    Homily on Book of Judges* 639, 657

    Interrogationes Sigewulfi in Genesin (by Alcuin)* 54, 339, 639

    Letter to the Monks of Eynsham 73

    Letter to Sigeweard, *De Veteri et Novo Testamento** 435e, 657

    Letter to Wulfgeat* 657

    – For other letters see Ker, *Catalogue*, p. 518 –

    Lives of Saints* 146f, 262f, 310e, 339, 355, 406, 476f

    *De paenitentia** 11

    Pastoral Letters* 11, 59.5, 65.5, 363, 644

    Pastoral Letters 59, 73, 800, 814

    *Pater noster** 322

    Prayers* 11

    *De temporibus anni** 11, 363e, 373, 380, 404f, 411e, 918e

    Vita S. Æthelwoldi 885.3

'Aesopus' (Hexametrical Romulus) 664

Æthelstan, king, Poems on 220, 342, 362

Æthelweard, ealdorman, *Chronicon* 349

Æthelwold, *see* Benedict of Nursia, and *Regularis Concordia*

Æthelwulf, poet, *De abbatibus* 555, 759

Aethicus Ister, *Cosmographia* 386, 439, 839

Pseudo-Aethicus, *see* Julius Honorius

Affinity, tables of 629

Ages of Man 56, 90, 385, 401, 451, 882, 913

Ages of the World* 55, 304, 389, 411, 435, 500, 637

Ages of the World 56, 65.5, 90, 304, 363, 380, 385, 451, 637, 882

Agroecius, *Ars de orthographia* 69.5

Alanus of Farfa, *Homiliarium* 423.9f

Alcuin

    De animae ratione 467, 749.5

Amalarius of Metz
  Liber officialis 40e, 59e, 61, 73e, 174, 394e, 741, 803, 925e
  (?) *Eclogae de ordine Romano* 73, 814
Pseudo-Amalarius, '*Regula canonicorum*', *see Institutio canonicorum*, under Capitularies
Ambrose
  De Abraham patriarcha 227e
  De apologia prophetae David 246.8, 550.5, 799, 832
  De bono mortis 227, 544
  De excessu fratris 227, 550.5, 606, 799
  De fide 593, 594.5, 605, 739
  De fuga saeculi 544
  De Isaac et anima 544
  De incarnationis dominicae sacramento 593, 605, 739
  De Jacob et vita beata 544
  De Joseph patriarcha 227, 550.5, 606, 799
  De morte Valentiniani 227, 544
  De mysteriis 246.8, 426, 434.5, 596, 881
  De Nabuthae 227, 463
  De obitu Theodosii 463
  De officiis ministrorum 543
  De paenitentia 20.1, 227, 550.5, 606, 799
  De paradiso 227, 544
  De Patriarchis 227, 550.5, 606, 799
  De sacramentis 426, 434.5, 596, 881
  De Spiritu Sancto 246.8e, 593, 594.5e, 605, 739
  De viduis 175.5, 596, 599, 881
  De virginibus 175.5, 596, 599, 881
  De virginitate 175.5, 596, 599, 881
  Epistolae 463, 550.5e, 799e
  Epistola ad Vercellensem ecclesiam 544, 581, 595.5
  In Evangelium Lucae 162, 516e
  Exhortatio virginitatis 175.5, 596, 599, 881
  Expositio de Psalmo CXVIII 175.1f, 653.2
  Hexameron 20, 61.5, 194, 778
  Excerpts from works 596
Pseudo-Ambrose
  De dignitate sacerdotali 434.5, 653.2
  De Protasio et Gervasio (*Epist.* 22) 463
  Fides S. Ambrosii 392
Ambrosiaster
  In Epistolas Pauli 594
  Quaestiones CXXVII Veteris et Novi Testamenti 706.5, 730
Ambrosius Autpertus
  De conflictu vitiorum et virtutum 519
  Admonition (from *De conflictu vitiorum et virtutum*) 41, 363
  Sermo de cupiditate 112

*Andreas*** 941
*Anglo-Saxon Chronicle** 52, 328⁺*, 357f, 364, 370.2, 372
(Animals) *Voces animantium* 188
Annales Cambriae 439
Annals of Christ Church, Canterbury* 411
Anonymus ad Cuimnanum, *Expossitio Latinitatis* 933
Ansegisus of Fontenelle, *see* Capitularies
Anselm of Canterbury, *Epistolae* 342.2
Anso of Lobbes, *Vita S. Ermini* 796.6f
Antiochia, *see* Bishops
Antiphons 174, 425, 548.1, 583
Antiphoners (Office antiphoners) 216.3f, 242.5, 277f, 307.2f, 610f, 666f, 675f, 777f,
    873f, 873.5f, 874f
Antonius Musa, *De herba vettonica* 402*, 527, 549, 633*, 831.4
Apocalypse of Thomas* 39
Apocrypha, *see* Abgar, Enoch, Gospel of Nicodemus
*Apollonius of Tyrus** 65.5
Ap(p)onius, *In Canticum canticorum* 802
Apostles, Burial places of 223
Apothegms, *see* Maxims
Apuleius, (?) *Peri hermenias* 67, 784.5
Pseudo-Apuleius, *Herbarius* 402*, 421*, 527, 549, 633*, 831.4
Arator
    Historia apostolica 12, 175, 280, 488, 523.5, 620.6f, 660, 890
    Poems on Arator 12
Aratus of Soli, *Phainomena* 186e ; *see* Cicero, *Aratea* ; Germanicus, *Aratea*
Aristoteles, *see* Boethius, Themistius
Arithmetic, *see* Boethius, Martianus Capella
Astronomical texts and illustrations 1.5, 85, 186, 230, 373, 398, 423, 428.4, 483, 845,
    919.3 ; *see also* Abbo of Fleury ; Aratus ; Hyginus ; Martianus Capella ; *De
    nominibus stellarum* ; Pseudo-Priscian, *Carmen de sideribus* ; Ptolemy
Athanasius 11.8
    Epistolae 552e
    (Evagrius) *Vita S. Antonii* 761
Atticus of Constantinople, (?) *Epistola formata* 254, 272, 671
Audax, *Excerpta* 809.9e
Augustine of Canterbury, *see* Gregory the Great
Augustine of Hippo
    Confessiones 163, 434
    Contra adversarium legis et prophetarum 164, 729
    Contra Faustum Manichaeum 550
    Contra Julianum 283, 551, 738
    Contra mendacium 164, 441.3f, 595.5, 600
    Contra sermonem Arianorum 164, 729
    De adulterinis coniugiis 164, 506, 729
    De agone Christiano 689, 710

De orthographia 69, 438, 809.9e
De schematibus et tropis 418.8f, 765
De tabernaculo 571, 578.5, 580, 690, 749, 875.4
De templo Salomonis 133
De temporibus 373e, 451e
De temporum ratione 85, 384, 478.5, 483, 492, 521.7f, 744, 784e, 818f, 856f, 902e
Epistola ad Wicthedum 85, 478.5, 483
Historia abbatum 433
Historia ecclesiastica 25, 75f, 181, 238, 367, 377, 401e, 410.5f, 427e, 487, 508e,
    555, 609e, 614e, 630, 759, 835e, 846, 856.2f, 863f, 885.3e
Saints' lives from *Historia ecclesiastica* : Æthelthryth 885.3 ; Aidan 614 ;
    Birinus 609, 885.3 ; Oswald 614, 885.3
Historia ecclesiastica ('Old English Bede')* 22, 39, 330e, 357f, 668, 673
Homiliae in Evangelia 274, 433e ; *see also* Paulus Diaconus, *Homiliarium*
In Apocalypsin 1, 225, 506, 685
In Canticum Habacuc 133
In Epistolas Catholicas 11.5, 607, 681
In Evangelium Lucae 134, 557, 706, 831.2f
In Proverbia Salomonis 604, 760
In Regum libros 133
In Tobiam 627
Nomina regionum locorumque de Actibus Apostolorum 601
Vita S. Cuthberti (prose) 56, 401, 427, 546, 586, 614, 885.3
    Vita S. Cuthberti (verse) 56, 401, 419, 427, 546, 586e, 614, 719.9, 815, 882, 913
Pseudo-Beda
De quindecim signis ante diem iudicii 330.5
Homily 508.5
Quaestionum super Genesin dialogus 791.6f
Benedicite, Commentary on 677.6
Benedict of Aniane, *see Memoriale Qualiter*
Benedict of Nursia
Regula 29, 41, 55, 101, 189, 363°, 363e, 379, 440, 631, 672, 758f
Regula (trans. Æthelwold)* 55, 248, 262f, 363e, 379, 672, 758f
See also Adrevald of Fleury, Simplicius, Smaragdus
'Benedictine Office'* 65.5, 644
Benedictionals 46, 202f?, 214.3, 259f, 286, 301, 302, 314, 400, 429, 504.3f, 585, 774.3,
    879, 880, 896, 914, 922, 923 ; Inscription for a Benedictional 314*
Benedictions (not in Benedictionals) 59, 70, 104, 406.5, 500, 583
Beowulf** 399
Berengarius of Tours, *Conversio Berengarii* (Recantation, in Gregory VII, *Registrum*
    VI.17a) 17, 179
Berengaudus, *In Apocalypsin* 155.5, 739.5f, 747.5f
Bernold of Constance, *Micrologus de ecclesiasticis observationibus* 73

Bible

    Bibles, complete or presumably complete originally   121f, 126f, 217, 245f, 249f,
        265.5e, 270, 289f, 293f, 410e, 448e, 449, 498.5f, 501.3f, 645.5f, 646f,
        825, 934 ; *see also* Florilegium

    Old Testament, Books in incomplete Bibles or individually copied :
        Leviticus   249f
        Numeri   498.5f, 646f
        Deuteronomium   538e (Greek and Latin), 646f
        Hexateuch*, *see* Ælfric of Eynsham
        Regum   265.5, 293f
        Ezra   305.5
        Tobias   583
        Job   305.5, 453.6, 840.5
        Psalms, *see* Psalter manuscripts
        Proverbia Salomonis   389°, 410, 919.3
        Ecclesiastes   410, 919.3
        Canticum canticorum   212.2, 289f, 410, 456.6, 919.3
        Sapientia   289f, 410, 919.3
        Ecclesiasticus   293f, 410, 470e, 501.3f
        Isaias   265.5
        Hieremias   265.5
        Ezechiel   6e, 265.5
        Daniel   126f, 265.5
        Minor prophets   121f, 265.5, 811f
        Libri Macchabaeorum   245f
        Book of Enoch (apocryphal)   459e
    New Testament   827.6
    Books of the New Testament :
        Actus Apostolorum   448f, 654 (Greek and Latin), 665
        Epistolae Pauli   173, 212.2, 524.8, 676, 892f
        Apocalypsis Johannis   212.2, 456.6, 528.1
        Gospels, *see* Gospel Books, Gospel harmony, Gospel lectionaries, Mass
            lectionaries
Note on Books of the Bible and the number of Psalms   56, 90, 385, 451, 882
Biblical commentaries, exegesis and glosses, anonymous or not identified   699, 792
    Decalogus Moysi, with exposition   800
    Psalms   451, 909
    Canticum canticorum   461, 474.6f ; 919.3 (from Alcuin)
    Gospels   808.2
    Gospel of Matthew   903
    Epistolae Pauli   782
    Epistola ad Colossenses   538e
    See also the commentaries by named authors
Biblical names, their etymologies and interpretations   230, 281.3f ; *see also* Eusebius of
    Caesarea, Jerome
Bibliotheca magnifica   12

Bili of Alet, *Vita S. Machuti* 482, 348*
(Birds) *Cantus avium* 439
Bishops, Anglo-Saxon, lists of
    Archbishops of Canterbury 364, 411
    Bishops of Sherborne 879
    Bishops of Winchester 304
    Bishops of several dioceses 44, 52, 56, 373, 385
Bishops of Alexandria, Antiochia, Jerusalem, and High priests of Jerusalem, listed 373
Blickling Homilies* 905
Boethius
    De consolatione Philosophiae 12, 12e, 23, 68°, 392e, 408f, 613.9, 671, 678f, 776,
        823, 829, 886, 887, 908 ; with accessus : 533, 899, 901 ; *see also* Alfred (trans.
        into Old English), Lupus of Ferrières, Remigius of Auxerre
    De institutione arithmetica 97, 669.4, 677.5, 886
    De institutione musica 72e, 784
    (trans.) Aristoteles, *Categoriae* 200.5f
    (trans.) Aristoteles, *De interpretatione* 269.1f
    Second Commentary on Porphyrius, *Isagoge* 67 ; *see also* Porphyrius
    In Categorias Aristotelis 269.1f
    In Topica Ciceronis 677.6
    Theological works 67
    Vitae Boethii 533, 671 ; *see also Epitaphium Helpis*
Pseudo-Boethius, *Geometria I* 185
Bonifatius
    Aenigmata 1.5, 12
    Ars grammatica 849.3f
    Epistolae 346f, 359e[+]*
    (?) Poem 845
Booklists 100*, 217, 326*, 529.1*, 555, 667, 774, 807, 829.8
Breton glosses 81, 538
Breviaries and Portiforium 104, 241.5f, 301.5f, 498f
Burchard of Worms, *Decretum* 317
Burginda, Letter of 802
Burial Office 583e
Byrhtferth of Ramsey
    Enchiridion[+]* 26e, 526
    Vita S. Ecgwini 344
    Vita S. Oswaldi 344
Byzantine emperors, list of 384

Caesarius of Arles
    Epistola 699
    In Apocalypsin 409, 628, 801
    Sermones 215e, 555e, 559e, 574e, 583e, 690e, 710e, 800e, 808e, 808.2e, 814e, 914

Calendars 26, 36, 104, 186, 248, 291, 306, 342, 380, 398, 400, 407, 478.5, 585, 611,
    617, 637, 641, 740, 791f, 855.5f, 888, 895f, 897, 912, 921, 944.8 ; Metrical
    calendars : 334, 337, 373, 641e ; 'Metrical calendar of York' : 385, 914
Cambridge Songs 12
Pseudo-Callisthenes, *see* Alexander the Great
Canon Law collections, papal decretals and Councils
    Canones Adamnani 361, 629
    Canones Apostolorum 272, 601.5
    Canones Wallici 361, 629
    Collectio canonum Hibernensis 59e, 81e, 361, 459e, 520.4f, 629
    Collectio Dionysio-Hadriana 629
    Collectio Sanblasiana 836
    Lanfranc's Collection 43, 144, 179, 258.3, 265, 272e, 601.5, 712
    Liber ex lege Moysi 81, 361
    Quadripartitus 592
    Sinodus episcoporum 81
    Various texts and excerpts 59, 73, 81, 179, 388, 583.3, 592, 644
    See also Councils and Synods ; Penitentials ; Atticus of Constantinople ; *also* Ælfric
        of Eynsham, Pastoral Letters ; Burchard of Worms ; *Decretum Pseudo-
        Gelasianum* ; Egbert, Dialogus ; Wulfstan I, Homilist, Canon Law Collection
Cantatorium 116, 597
Canterbury, St Augustine's, Privileges for 387
Canterbury, archbishops, Memorandum on their primacy 342.2
Canticles (for the daily Offices) 4°, 77, 104, 106, 148, 150f, 291°, 304°, 306, 333e, 334,
    381°, 407°, 425, 430, 450e°, 451°, 499°, 517°, 538 (Greek and Latin), 617, 655,
    740°, 754, 790, 891, 912, 920, 939 ; *see also* Monastic canticles
Caper, *De orthographia* 69.5
Capitularies and related texts
    Acta praeliminaria of Council of Aachen (816) 926
    Admonitio generalis (789) 73e, 925e
    Capitulare monasticum (818/819?) 29, 41, 363, 379, 440
    Institutio canonicorum (Aachen Council, 816) 73e, 925e ; *see also* Wulfstan I
    Ansegisus, *Capitularium collectio* 73e, 629e ; *Capitularium Collectio* ii.33
        (De festivitatibus anni) 41, 363, 379, 440
    Gerbald of Liège, First Capitulary 73, 592, 879, 896, 922
    Excerpts from Capitularies 73e, 925e
Carmen de sideribus, *see* Pseudo-Priscian
Cartularies 344.5f, 366
Cassian (Johannes Cassianus)
    Collationes 516e, 627e, 700e
    De institutis monachorum 152e, 528
Cassiodorus
    De anima 581
    (?) *De computo paschali* 311
    De orthographia 69.5
    Historia tripartita 2f

In Psalmos 77e, 154f ; 237 and 822f abbreviated
Institutiones I   263, 573, 713 ; II   185e
'Cato'
    Cato novus   252, 664
    Disticha Catonis   12, 190, 389, 664 ; 182* ; *see also* Remigius of Auxerre
    Monosticha Catonis   120e
Pseudo-Censorinus, *De geometria*   185e
Charlemagne, Letter to Michael Paleologus   417
Charms in Latin   395.5, 411, 421, 432, 450, 541, 555, 642, 765
Charms in Old English*   39, 59, 102, 308, 333, 363, 407, 411, 421 (*Lacnunga*),
    537, 642, 765
Charters (excluding all single-leaf documents)   346f, 382 ; *see also* Records
Christ, Note on   451 ; on length of his body   380
Christ's incarnation, Note on   56, 90, 451
Christ I and *III***   257
*Christ and Satan***   640
Chrodegang of Metz, *Regula canonicorum* (enlarged version)   60, 206f, 288f, 808 ;
    59.5e*, 60*, 206f*, 288f*
Chronology, Notes on   56, 451
Chrysostomus, *see* Johannes Chrysostomus
Cicero
    Aratea   186, 373, 398e, 423, 428.4
    De inventione   216.6
    In Catilinam   254
    Philippicae   907.5
    Somnium Scipionis (from *De re publica*)   1.5, 536 ; *see also* Macrobius
    Topica   677.6f ; *see also* Boethius
Pseudo-Cicero
    Synonyma   541
    and Sallust (?), *Invectivae*   1.5, 254, 439
Pseudo-Clement (Rufinus), *Recognitiones*   692.5
Collectars   104, 212.3f, 223, 380, 431
Collects from Mass and Office   118, 118.5, 450
Colloquies and conversation phrases   583, 608, 686, 784 ; *see also* Ælfric Bata, Ælfric
    of Eynsham
Pseudo-Columbanus (Pseudo-Alcuin), *Praecepta vivendi*   12, 120, 324, 488, 815, 890
Computus
    Computus materials in prose and verse, and computus tables   26, 30.5f, 36, 70, 85,
        104, 111[(*)], 186, 230, 258, 282, 306, 311, 321.5, 326, 333, 334, 342, 363.2, 392,
        398, 400, 404*, 407[(*)], 411[(*)], 435, 439, 440, 478.5, 483, 498.8, 526, 538, 541,
        583, 611, 612, 637, 740, 744, 888, 897, 912, 919.3, 921
    Canterbury Computus   411, 611
    Leofric-Tiberius Computus   373, 585
    Winchester Computus   186, 304, 378f, 380
    See also Ælfric of Eynsham, Beda, Byrhtferth, Dionysius Exiguus, Hermannus
        Contractus, Hrabanus Maurus

De dominica oratione   595.5, 699
De mortalitate   699
De opere et eleemosynis   699
Epistolae   297f
Cyprianus Gallus, *Pentateuchos*   159

Damasus
Epigram for the basilica of St. Agnes   38, 680
Verses on St. Paul   53
Pseudo-Damasus and Pseudo-Jerome, Colloquy on celebrating Mass   411*, 500⁺*
*Daniel***   640
Decalogus Moysi, *see* Biblical Commentaries
Decretum Pseudo-Gelasianum de libris recipiendis et non recipiendis   263, 573, 713, 749.5, 800, 808.2
Defensor of Ligugé, *Liber Scintillarum*   34.1, 59e, 470°
*Deor***   257
Devil's account of the next world*   363
Dialectic
Treatise on Dialectic   807
See also Alcuin, Augustine, Martianus Capella
Didymus (Jerome), *De Spiritu Sancto*   266.5
Dies Aegyptiaci   174, 186, 404*, 421*, 483, 498.1 ; *see also* Prognostics
Dionysius Exiguus
Cyclus Paschalis magnus   26, 856
Epistola de ratione Paschae   329.5f, 611
Dionysius Periegetes, *see* Priscian
Pseudo-Dioscorides
Liber medicinae ex herbis femininis   402e*, 421e*, 527, 549, 633e*
Curae herbarum   402e*, 421e*, 633e*
Disciples of Christ   56, 373, 385
Disticha Catonis, see Cato
Documents, *see* Charters, Manumissions, Records
Domesday Inquest and related texts
Great Domesday Book   521.5
Little Domesday Book   521.4
Exon Domesday   256
Domesday monachorum   205.5
Donation inscription (in books given to Exeter Cathedral by Bishop Leofric)⁺*   15, 39, 174, 530, 533, 534, 537, 585, 590
Donatus, *Ars maior*   321, 829e ; *see also* Anonymus ad Cuimnanum, Pompeius, Remigius of Auxerre, Sergius
*Dream of the Rood***   941
Dudo of Saint-Quentin, *Historia Normannorum*   80
Dunchad (Martin of Laon?), Commentary on Martianus Capella   48, 96, 490e

Dungal
    Carmina 120e
    Epistolae 417, 483e
Dunstan
    Poems 175e, 188, 538
    Letter to Dunstan 879
    See also Adelard of Ghent, 'B', Osbern of Canterbury
De duodecim abusivis saeculi 750

'De ecclesiastica consuetudine' (excerpts from Amalarius and *Regularis Concordia*) 59, 925
Ecclesiastical institutes[*] 341
De ecclesiasticis gradibus 59, 59.5*, 65.5*, 73, 223°, 644, 800, 814 ; *see also* Severus
'Eddius Stephanus', *see* Stephen of Ripon
Edward the Confessor, Letter to 592
Egbert, archbishop of York
    Dialogus ecclesiasticae institutionis 398
    Works attributed : *see* Penitentials, Wulfstan I, Homilist
Eligius of Noyon, (?) Florilegium 851.6
Encomium Emmae Reginae 287
Ennodius, *Dictiones, Epistolae, Poemata* 513
Enoch, Book of, *see* Bible, Old Testament
Epaphroditus, Excerpta geometrica 185
Ephraem Syrus
    De compunctione cordis 510
    Sermones 2.8
Epiphanius, (?) *De mensuris et ponderibus* 483
Epitaphium Helpis (wife of Boethius) 193
Epitaphium Vitalis, *see* Vitalis
Ernulf of Rochester, *De incestis coniugibus* 808.1
Eucharist, Miracle stories on 749.5
Eucherius of Lyon, *Formulae spiritalis intelligentiae* 516e, 947f
Euclid, *Euclides latinus* 185e, 615e
Eugenius of Toledo, (?)*Heptametron de primordio mundi* 12, 829.8, 903
Eusebius of Caesarea
    (Rufinus) *Historia ecclesiastica* 57, 61e, 137e, 768, 773.5f
    (Jerome) *De situ et nominibus locorum Hebraicorum* (*Onomasticon*) 230, 601
Eusebius (= Hwætberht of Monkwearmouth-Jarrow?), *Aenigmata* 12, 478
Eusebius Gallicanus, *Sermones* 426e, 574e
Pseudo-Eusebius Gallicanus, *Sermones* 783e, 800e
Eutropius, *Breviarium historiae Romanae* 428.5 ; with additions and continuation by Paulus Diaconus ('*Historia Romana*') 79, 199
Eutyches, *Ars de verbo* 538
Eutychianos (Paulus Diaconus of Naples), *Theophili Actus* 433.3
Evangelists, Poem on 531

Gaius, *Institutiones*, bk. i   629
Galen
    Ad Glauconem de medendi methodo   145
    Epistola de febribus   498.1
    Liber tertius   145
    (?) *De podagra*   145
Gaudentius of Brescia, *Tractatus*   669f
Gauzlin of Fleury
    Letter to king Robert of France   230
    Epitaphium Gauzlini   886
Gelasius I, pope, *see Decretum Pseudo-Gelasianum*
Genesis**   640
Gennadius
    Liber ecclesiasticorum dogmatum   246.8, 475e, 749.5, 787
    De viris illustribus   263, 573, 713
    De viris illustribus, ch. xiii (on Prudentius)   38, 70, 246
Geography and Cosmography, *see* Aethicus Ister ; Isidore, *Etymologiae* ; Julius
    Honorius ; Map of the World ; Orosius (*Historiae*, bk. i) ; Priscian, *Periegesis* ;
    Sigeric
Geometry
    Texts and collections   185, 230, 615
    See also Pseudo-Boethius, Pseudo-Censorinus, Epaphroditus, Euclid, Radulf of
        Liège, Vitruvius Rufus, *and see* Weights and measures
Gerbald (Ghaerbald) of Liège, *see* Capitularies
Germanicus, *Aratea*   1.5
Gesta Ludovici imperatoris (Louis II)   252
Gildas, *De excidio Britanniae*   396
Glastonbury, List of abbots   373
Gloria, Notes and interpretations of   378, 380
Glossaries and collections of glosses
    Latin and (wholly or partly) Old English   45, 56, 319, 326, 360, 377, 414, 436, 535,
        541, 555, 775, 807, 824 ; *see also* Ælfric of Eynsham
    Latin-Latin   93, 96, 98, 329.5f, 389, 435, 438, 775, 792, 807, 908 ; *see also Liber*
        glossarum
    Greek-Latin   438, 541 ; *see also* Glossarial poems, *Hermeneumata Pseudo-*
        Dositheana, Scholica Graecarum glossarum
Glossarial poems on Greek medical terminology   765
Goscelin of Canterbury, Lives of Anglo-Saxon Saints :
    Æthelburga 216 ; Augustine of Canterbury (Vita, Miracula, Translatio) 387 ;
    Archbishop Deusdedit 387, 424 ; Abbot Hadrian 387, 424 ; Archbishop Honorius 387, 424 ;
    Archbishop Justus 387, 424 ; (?)Kenelm (Vita brevior) 100 ; Archbishop Laurentius 387, 424 ;
    Letardus (Vita) 387, (Miracula) 457 ; Archbishop Mellitus 387 ; Mildred (Vita and Translatio)
    348f, 387, 424 ; Archbishop Theodore 387, 424 ; Wulfhilda 216
    (?)*Libellus contra usurpatores S. Mildrethae*   387

Gospel Books   19e, 21e, 28e, 63f, 83, 119, 124f, 138, 149, 172, 213, 214, 218f, 219, 220,
    221f, 266, 269, 275f, 279, 281.5f, 290, 295, 299, 302.3f, 316.1, 343, 354f, 362,
    368.2f, 374f, 413, 432e, 442.3f, 444, 445, 446, 447, 448, 450e, 501, 521, 529, 530,
    531, 532, 554, 645.5f, 647.5e, 677f, 688, 694, 761.5f, 770f, 774, 776.2, 794, 796,
    798, 808.3f, 809, 812, 827.2f, 827.7, 829.5, 830.5f, 831, 840f, 877, 878, 893, 900,
    904f, 906, 907, 919.6, 930, 931f, 937, 940, 940f, 945
Gospels not in complete Gospel Books
    Luke   21, 221f, 647.5, 664.5
    John   21, 165, 368.2f, 380e, 453.8, 501.2, 647.5, 664.5
Gospel harmony   640.1f, 827.6
Gospel lectionaries   118, 118.5, 139, 248, 316.1, 500, 502f, 522e, 651, 827, 942 ; *see
    also* Mass lectionaries
Gospel lists and pericope notes   119, 149, 172, 279, 290, 295, 362, 413, 447, 501, 530,
    554, 570.1e, 809, 831, 866.5, 877, 942
Gospel and Epistle lists   522f, 944.8
Gospels in Old English ('West-Saxon Gospels')*   15, 44, 358, 577, 621f, 859f ; *see also*
    Passion story*
Gospel of Nicodemus   459, 930.5 ; 15*, 39*
Graduals   30.8f, 132.3f, 216.4f, 251, 416f, 457.6f, 597, 874.3f, 936.9f ; *see also*
    Sequences, Tropers
Grammar, anonymous texts and notes
    Treatises   321, 336, 435, 765
    Dialogue on declinations   244, 331, 414
    Notes   7, 93, 182, 236, 263e, 435, 629, 882, 918
    Glossary of grammatical terms   438
    See also Ælfric, Agroecius, Alcuin, Anonymous ad Cuimnanum, Audax, Beda,
        Bonfatius, Caper, Cassiodorus, Donatus, Eutyches, *Excerptiones de Prisciano*,
        Isidore (*Etymologiae*), Martianus Capella, Phocas, Pompeius, Priscian, Sergius
Gratianus Augustus (Roman emperor), *Epistola ad Ambrosium*   593, 594.5, 605
Greek, *see* Alphabets, Creeds, Glossaries, *Sanctus*, and nos. 12, 538, 654, 784, 903
Gregorius Nazianzenus (Rufinus)
    Liber apologeticus (*Oratio* 2)   689
    De Hieremiae prophetae dictis (*Oratio* 17)   699
    Orationes   714
Gregory the Great
    Dialogi   34, 208f, 510, 667, 715, 856.1f, 924e, 937.3, 943.8f
    Dialogi, trans. Werferth, in Old English*   92, 207f, 359, 632
    Homiliae in Evangelia   42e, 242, 255f, 566, 733, 767, 804.5f
    Homiliae in Ezechielem   6, 147, 247, 464.9e, 505, 558, 589, 760, 831.6, 911, 944.5
    Moralia   166e, 241e, 453.6, 469.3, 564, 668.5f, 677.3f, 691e, 704, 773.6, 773.7,
        840.5e, 858f, 865.5f, 946.5e ; *see also* Adalbert of Metz, Laidcenn, Lanfranc
    Registrum epistolarum   17, 70f, 240, 272e, 469.5, 556
    Regula Pastoralis   99, 261, 346f (abridged), 439.6f, 590, 598, 684, 742, 755.5, 771f,
        800e, 833, 894, 898.5e ; *see also* Alfred (trans. into Old English)
    Gregory and Augustine of Canterbury, *Libellus responsionum*   90, 387, 565, 583.3e,
        919.3e ; *see also* Beda, *Historia ecclesiastica* (I.xxvii)

(?) *Symbolum fidei*   17, 240, 392?, 469.5, 556
(?) *De iuramentis episcoporum*   742
See also Paterius, Johannes Diaconus, and no. 844
Gregory VII, pope, *Registrum*, see Berengarius, *Conversio*
Gregory of Tours
    Historia Francorum   264e, 782e, 915e ; II.1 (*Vita S. Bricii*)   264, 915
    Libri miraculorum   198.5
    De virtutibus S. Martini   264e, 689e, 774.1f, 915e
Guido of Arezzo, *Micrologus*   230e
Guitmund of Aversa, *Confessio de S. Trinitate*   264
Guthlac Poems**   257

Haimo of Auxerre
    Homiliarium   242, 524.6f
    In Canticum canticorum   155.5
    See also Remigius of Auxerre
Harrowing of Hell   28
Hebrew, see Alphabets, Eusebius of Caesarea, Jerome
'Hegesippus', see Josephus
Heiric of Auxerre, *Collectanea*   281.3
Heito of Reichenau, *Visio Wettini*   508
Heliand, in Old Saxon   308
Helperic of Auxerre, *De computo*   186, 321.5, 478.5, 483, 743
'Heraclides', see Palladius
Herbarius, enlarged version   402*, 421e*, 527, 549, 633* ; see also Pseudo-Apuleius
Hereford diocesan boundaries*   139
Hermannus Archidiaconus, (?) *Miracula S. Eadmundi*   371, 881.7
Hermannus Contractus of Reichenau, *Computus*   411e
Hermeneumata Pseudo-Dositheana   807
Hexateuch*, see Ælfric of Eynsham
Hieronymus, see Jerome
Hilarius, (?)*Epistola ad Augustinum de querela Gallorum*   805.5
Hilduin of Saint-Denis, *Passio S. Dionysii*   582
Hisperic poems, see *Adelphus*, *Rubisca*
Historia de S. Cuthberto, see Cuthbert
Homiletic fragment**   941
Homiliaries, Latin   498.0f, *and see* Alanus of Farfa, Paulus Diaconus, Haimo of
    Auxerre ; see also Smaragdus, *Expositio libri comitis*
Homiliaries, Old English, see Ker, *Catalogue*, p. 527, *and* Homilies, *below*
Homiliarium of Saint-Père, Chartres   131, 200f, 461e
Homilies and sermons in Latin, anonymous or not identified   17, 51, 118, 153, 175.5,
    189, 242, 376, 378+*, 388, 406.5, 418, 461, 539, 574, 609, 782, 804, 925

Homilies and sermons in Old English, anonymous*   18, 39, 44, 50, 59.5, 64, 65.5, 66,
    108, 109, 117f, 294, 322, 356f, 359, 366, 376, 520, 524.2f, 538.5, 569, 638, 642,
    644, 879, 905, 941 ; *see also* Ælfric of Eynsham, Wulfstan I, Homilist, and the
    detailed index in Ker, *Catalogue*, pp. 527-536
Horace
    Epistolae 252e
    Carmina 12e
Hormisdas, pope, (?)*Epistola per universas provincias* 583.3
Horologium 914
Hrabanus Maurus
    De computo 258, 398
    De institutione clericorum (II.1-10) 59, 65.5e*, 131, 644e* ; (II.1-7) 73
    De laudibus s. crucis 12, 178, 919.3e
    De universo 749e
    In Epistolas Pauli 140e
    In Hester 779
    In Judith 779
    In Matthaeum 243
Hucbald of Saint-Amand
    De harmonica institutione 12
    Ecloga de calvis 12, 196
Hugo of Langres, Commentary on the Psalms 306.5
Human body (Note on the number of bones, veins and teeth) 56, 90, 385, 451, 882
*Husband's message*** 257
Hwætberht, *see* Eusebius
Hyginus Mythographus, (*Poetica*)*Astronomica* 1.5, 186e, 423e, 428.4, 483e
Hyginus Gromaticus, *De limitibus* 185
Hymnals 104, 244, 291, 381e, 391, 431, 696f, 914, 920 ; *see also* Expositio hymnorum
Hymns (Office hymns not in hymnals) 7, 12, 28, 51, 56, 196?, 306.5, 333, 392, 406.5,
    450, 474.5, 482, 514, 865.1, 865.2
Hymnus trium puerorum (in verse) 927

Ilias latina 535, 664
Immaculate conception, Note on, *see* Virgin Mary
De initio creaturae, *see* Ages of the World* in no. 435
Irish charms 421
Irish glosses 7, 81, 148
Isembard of Fleury, *Inventio et Miracula S. Judoci* 474.5
Isidore of Seville
    Allegoriae sacrae Scripturae 263, 573, 578, 713, 742, 780, 818.5, 851.6
    De ecclesiasticis officiis 263e, 391e, 713e, 845
    De fide catholica 188.8, 460, 467e, 568e, 575
    De natura rerum 85e, 258, 326, 398, 536, 786, 943.4f
    De ortu et obitu patrum 263, 573, 578, 713, 742, 780, 818.5, 845, 851.6
    De viris illustribus 263, 573, 713

Differentiae 188.8e, 460e, 787, 845e, 932f
Etymologiae 154.5f, 176e, 185e, 188.8e, 311e, 442.4e, 460e, 469, 497.2e, 498.1f,
    524.4f, 561, 682, 690e, 784.5e, 821f, 885f, 889, 919.3e
Prooemia Veteris et Novi Testamenti 263, 573, 578, 713, 742, 780, 845, 851.6
Quaestiones in Vetus Testamentum 168, 453.2, 716, 736, 944.3
Sententiae 470e, 515, 773f, 848.8f
Synonyma 114, 363e*, 392, 415, 461, 752, 845, 946
(?) Versus in bibliotheca 87
Excerpts 800, 814
Pseudo-Isidore, De ordine creaturarum 785, 894
Israel the Grammarian, De arte metrica 765, 903
Ivo of Chartres, Sermones 748

Jerome
    Adversus Helvidium 229
    Altercatio Luciferani et Orthodoxi 832
    Contra Jovinianum 426, 544, 805.5
    Contra Vigilantium 229
    De viris illustribus 263, 311, 573, 713
    Epistolae 2.5, 229, 230, 264, 832, 845
    Hebraicae quaestiones in Genesin 230, 601
    In Danielem 161, 434.5, 571, 849f
    In Ecclesiasten 832, 944
    In Ezechielem 662
    In Hieremiam 453.4, 702
    In Prophetas minores 11.8, 161, 228, 620.3
    In Evangelium Matthaei 755f, 770.5f
    In Epistolas Pauli 453.2e, 829.2f
    Liber interpretationis Hebraicorum nominum 230, 601, 659
    Tractatus in Psalmos 136, 455, 943.6f
    Vita S. Hilarionis 761
    Vita S. Malchi 359
    Vita S. Pauli Eremitae 103, 311, 761
    (?) Notae divinae legis necessariae 230
    Excerpts 61, 281.3, 516, 800, 814
    Jerome and Orosius, Excerpta de situ Babylonis 555, 759
    See also Didymus, Eusebius, Origines, Victorinus of Pettau
Pseudo-Jerome
    Breviarium in Psalmos 453e, 455e, 914
    De diversis generibus musicorum (Epist. supp. 23) 475, 601
    De duodecim scriptoribus 749.5
    De essentia divinitatis (Epist. supp. 14) 246.8, 690
    De fide catholica 552
    De quindecim signis ante diem iudicii 330.5
    De sex civitatibus ad quas homicida fugit 230

Kentish Hymn** 389
Kentish Psalm** 389
Kings : their titles in six languages 223
Kings of Anglo-Saxon England, *see* Royal genealogies
Kyriale 251

Lactantius, *De phoenice* 12, 535
Laidcenn
    Ecloga de Moralibus in Job 135
    Lorica 28°, 421, 432
Lanfranc of Bec
    Constitutiones 248, 268.2
    Epistolae 43e, 342.2
    Gloss on Epistolae Pauli 212.2, 524.8
    Notes on Augustine, *De civitate Dei* 236
    Notes on Gregory the Great, *Moralia* 469.3
    Notes on the translations of Plato's *Timaeus* 236
    Lanfranc's Epitaph 342.3
    See also Acta Lanfranci ; Canon law collections ; Papal letters in no. 179
Languages of the World, Note on 114, 500, 829.8
Lantfred of Winchester, *Translatio et miracula S. Swithuni* 344, 496, 885.3, 927
Lapidary* 363
Laudes regiae 251, 406.5, 714
Laws of the Anglo-Saxon kings and related texts* 52, 59.5, 73, 307f, 314, 340, 341,
    345, 357f, 917 ; *for detailed inventory see* Ker, *Catalogue*, pp. 538-9
Lectionary 277.3f ; *see* Gospel lectionaries, Mass lectionaries, Office lectionaries,
    legendaries
Legendaries (Passionals) 36, 344, 754.5, 754.6 ; *see also* Ælfric of Eynsham, Lives of
    Saints
Leofric of Exeter, Inventory of his donations* 15, 530 ; *see also* Donation inscription
Leontius of Naples (Anastasius Bibliothecarius), *Vita Johannis Eleemosynarii* 267, 865
Letald of Micy, *Vita S. Juliani* 586
Letters, collections : mainly to Archbishops of Canterbury 368, to Anglo-Saxon
    bishops 383
Libellus de mensuris 185
Liber glossarum 700.2f
Liber monstrorum 493
Liber Pontificalis 230e
Liberal arts and sciences, Treatises and poems on their system 12, 337, 483, 765, 784.5 ;
    see also Arithmetic, Astronomy, Dialectic, Geometry, Grammar, Music, Rhetoric
Libri Vitae, *see* Confraternity Books
Pseudo-Linus, *Martyrium S. Petri et Pauli* 684
Litanies 4, 77, 106, 291, 304, 333, 334 (Greek), 376, 378, 380, 425, 430, 450, 617, 655,
    754, 891, 903 (Greek), 912, 920

Liturgical books, *see* Antiphoners, Benedictionals, Breviaries, Calendars, Cantatorium, Collectars, Gospel Books, Gospel lectionaries, Graduals, Homiliaries, Hymnals, Kyriale, Legendaries, Manual services, Martyrology, Mass lectionaries, Missals, Office lectionaries, Pontificals, Prayerbooks, Psalter collects, Psalter manuscripts, Responsoriale, Sacramentaries, Service books, Tonary, Tropers

Liturgy : Directions and expositions relating to Mass and Office, and to other services and private devotions   29, 59, 59.5, 73, 248, 281.3, 380, 411, 500, 736, 814, 919.3 ; *see also* 'Benedictine Office'*, Consuetudinaries, Expositio missae, Ordo Romanus, and commentaries by known authors, especially Ælfric of Eynsham, Amalarius, Bernold of Constance, Hrabanus Maurus

Lunarium 111⁺*   304, 380, 498.1

Lupus of Ferrières
    De metris Boethii   193, 533, 613.9f, 671, 829
    Sermon   474.5

Macrobius
    In Somnium Scipionis   1.5f, 373e, 423e, 428.4e, 536
    Saturnalia   402.5e, 439
Mambres and Jannes⁺*   373
Manual Services   111, 656
Manumissions*   44, 354, 445
Map of the World   373
Marbod of Rennes
    Passio S. Mauricii sociorumque   689
    Poem   252
Marianus Scotus, *Chronicon*   342.6
Martial, Epigram I.xix   195
Martianus Capella, *De nuptiis Philologiae et Mercurii*   48, 95, 373e, 423e, 428.4e ; bk. iv : 67, 438 ; bk. viii : 186, 428.4 ; *see also* Remigius of Auxerre
Martin of Laon, *see* Dunchad
'Martinellus'   264, 296, 378.5, 782, 915
Martinus of Braga, *Formula honestae vitae*   112
Martyrologium (by Usuard of Saint-Germain-des-Prés)   41, 66f, 248, 405
Martyrology, Old English*   39f, 62, 282f, 298f, 338
Marvels of the East (*Mirabilia*)   373⁺*, 399*
Mass texts (not in missals or sacramentaries)
    Mass chants   106, 433.2, 526
    Masses and mass prayers   111, 223, 291, 363.2, 435, 557f, 774.3, 919.3
    Mass of the Dead   879e, of the Holy Trinity   291, of the Virgin   389e
    Masses for saints (not in missals) : Alban 865.1 ; Birinus 609 ; Cuthbert 56, 155 ; Dunstan 94 ; Eadmund 514 ; Germanus 583 ; Judoc 474.5 ; Nicholas 344
    See also Missals, Sacramentaries, Graduals, Tropers, and *Expositio missae*, Liturgy
Mass lectionaries   120.6f, 224f, 870f, 872.5f ; *see also* Gospel lectionaries, Gospel lists, Gospel and Epistle lists
Mathematics, *see* Arithmetic, Geometry

Maxims, Proverbs, Sentences and Apothegms   93, 182*, 244⁺*, 257*, 331⁺*, 370.2*,
      451⁺*, 898, 903
Measures, *see* Weights and Measures
Medicina de Quadrupedibus   402*, 421*, 549, 633*
Medicine
      Medical texts   12, 145, 222.3, 498.1, 498.7, 498.9
      Medical handbook (Bald's Leechbook)*   479
      Medical recipes   12, 70, 98, 498.1 ; Veterinary recipes   407
      Medical recipes*   39, 326, 333, 402, 412, 421 (*Lacnunga*), 523f, 848f
      Liber Aurelii de acutis passionibus   145
      Liber Esculapii de chronicis passionibus   145
      'Petrocellus'   12e, 498.9, 855
      Poems on Greek medical terminology   765
      Treatise on cauterization   498.9
      Tract on the temperaments   919.3
      Treatise on urines   498.1
      See also Galen, Serenus, Soranus ; *also* Charms, Human body, and the collections
          of texts in nos. 402, 421, 527, 549, 633, 831.4
Memoriale qualiter (by Benedict of Aniane?)   29, 41, 363e°, 379, 440, 926
*Menologium***   370.2
Pseudo-Methodius, *Revelationes*   463.5, 749
Metre, *see* Versification
Metrical calendar, *see* Calendars
Metrology, *see* Weights and measures
Milo of Saint-Amand, *Carmen de sobrietate*   12
Mildred, bishop, *see* Sylloge
Missals   120.3f, 121.5f, 127.6f, 143.5f, 212f, 258.8f, 299.5f, 418.3f, 423.3f, 454f, 456.2f,
      498.3f, 504.4f, 524f, 572f, 585, 649f, 668.9f, 756.5f, 764e, 789f, 796.3f, 816.3f, 837,
      871f, 871.5f, 872f, 874.6f, 875f, 875.5f, 875.6f, 936f, 936.1f, 936.4f, 936.5f, 937.1f ;
      see also Sacramentaries
Modoin of Autun, *Ecloga* (for Charlemagne)   280
Monastic canticles   104, 244, 291, 337°, 391°, 920
Months, Macedonian names of   136
Mulberry tree, Treatise on*   402, 421, 633
Muses, verses on, and list   95
Music
      Commemoratio brevis de tonis   72
      Musica Enchiriadis   72
      Scolica Enchiriadis   72
      Excerpts   230
      See also Boethius, Guido of Arezzo, Hucbald of Saint-Amand, Martianus Capella
Musical notation, in numerous manuscripts, has not been recorded in the Handlist

Nations, Characterization of 435
Necrologies and obits 41, 248, 342.8f, 380, 405, 637
Nemesianus, *Cynegetica* 884
'Nennius', *Historia Brittonum* 439
Nicetas of Remesiana, (?)*De lapsu virginis consecratae* 175.5, 596, 599, 881
Nicodemus, *see* Gospel of Nicodemus
Noah and Old Testament figures, Note on* 300, 363, 411
Noah's Ark, its dimensions 56, 90, 363*, 385, 435*, 451, 882
De nominibus stellarum 423, 428.4
Norman Anonymous, Tracts 107
Normandy, List of Dukes 486 ; *see also* William of Jumièges
Notae iuris 223

Obits, *see* Necrologies
Oda, archbishop of Canterbury, *Constitutiones* 383
Odilo of Cluny, *Sermones* 175.5e
Odo of Cluny
    Occupatio 903
    Sermon 865.4
Odo of Glanfeuil (Pseudo-Faustus), *Vita S. Mauri* 264
Office
    Offices and Office texts 111, 223, 424.5f, 425 ; *see also* Breviaries, Collectars
    Office chants 39, 77, 104, 323, 464.9, 548.1, 583, 829.8 ; *see also* Antiphoners,
        Hymnals, Responsoriale
    Office lectionaries and Office lessons 268.6f, 345f, 457, 496, 757f, 769, 809.8 ;
    see also Homiliaries, Legendaries
Office of All Saints 363
Office of the Dead 51e, 291e, 406.5e, 425e, 548.1e
Office of the Holy Cross 380
Office of the Trinity 380, 617
Office of the Virgin 363, 380, 451
Offices of Saints : Alban 865.1 ; Augustine of Canterbury 153e, 389e, 409e ;
    Benedict 427 ; Birinus 865.4e ; Cuthbert 56, 427, 913f ; Eadmund 813 ; Guthlac
    64e, 427 ; Hadrian 153e ; Julian 586e ; Katherine 548.1 ; Machutus 482e ; Mary
    Magdalene 742 ; Nicholas 155e, 344 ; Stephen (Invention) 435e
Old High German, Poems partly in 12
Old Saxon, *see Heliand*
Old Testament figures, *see* Noah
Optatianus Porphyrius, *Carmina* 246e, 805e
Oracle, pagan (Greek) 654
Ordeals 104, *and see* Pontificals, *also* no. 223
Ordo Romanus XIIIA 59, 919.3, 925
Ordo Romanus XXXII 61

Origenes, *Homiliae* :
  (Rufinus) *In Genesin* 239 ; *In Exodum* 239, 745 ; *In Leviticum* 239, 669f, 745 ;
    In Numeros 455e ; *In Josue* 239 ; *In Judices* 239 ; *In libros Regum* 239
  (Jerome) *In Canticum canticorum* 229, 239 ; *In Isaiam* 239 ; *In Hieremiam* 239 ;
    In Ezechielem 239
Orosius
  Historiae adversus paganos   32, 35.5f, 196.5, 259.5f, 281.3e, 555e, 820f
  Historiae adversus paganos, Old English version*   300, 370, 622f, 916f
Pseudo-Orosius, *see* Pseudo-Augustine
Orthographia, *see* Agroecius, Alcuin, Beda, Caper ; *see also* Grammar
Osbern of Canterbury
  Vita et Translatio S. Ælphegi   350
  Vita S. Dunstani   94, 303
Otloh of St. Emmeram, *Vita S. Nicholai*   434.5
Ovid
  Amores   664e, 903e
  Ars amatoria   538e, 903e
  Metamorphoses   919e
Pseudo-Ovid
  De nuce   535
  Argumenta to Vergil's *Georgica* and *Aeneid*   919

Palladius of Hellenopolis, *Historia Lausiaca* ('Heraclides', *Paradisus*)   251.5, 267
Papal letters   144, 179, 383, 592, 879 ; *see also* Sergius I
Paris Psalter**   891
Pascha Christianorum, Note on   451
Paschasius Radbertus
  De assumptione B. M. V.   2.8, 175.5, 264
  De corpore et sanguine Domini   251.5, 474
Passion story*   608.5f
Passionals, *see* Legendaries
Pastor Hermas   819f
Pater noster   65.5**, 334 (Greek), 450°, 903 (metrical version) ; *for prose versions in
  Old English see* Ælfric of Eynsham ; Gospels in Old English
Paterius, *De expositione Veteris et Novi Testamenti* (excerpts from works of Gregory
  the Great)   772f
Patrick, Saint, *Epistola ad episcopos*   361
Paulinus of Nola, *Carmina natalitia*   847e, 910e
Paulus Diaconus of Montecassino
  Historia Langobardorum   485
  Homiliarium   16, 24, 129, 130, 209f, 222, 226, 249.3f, 273, 424, 452, 753, 763,
    763.1, 763.2, 930.5e
  See also Eutropius
Paulus Diaconus of Naples, *see* Eutychianos
Pelagius, *In Epistolam Pauli ad Philippenses*   793f

Penitential literature
    Penitential of Pseudo-Beda-Egbert   459
    Poenitentiale Cummeani   565, 583.3
    Poenitentiale Egberti   73e, 592, 911.5e ; Prologue only 583.3, 879, 896, 922, 925
    Dialogus Egberti, see Egbert
    Penitential of Halitgar of Cambrai   581
    Poenitentiale Oxoniense I   565
    Poenitentiale Oxoniense II   565
    Poenitentiale Remense   565, 656e
    Poenitentiale Sangermanense   90
    Poenitentiale Theodori   73e, 90, 393, 565e, 656e
    Judicia Theodori G (*Canones Gregorii*)   565
    Poenitentiale Pseudo-Theodori   59, 808
    Penitential ('*Confessionale Pseudo-Egberti*')*   59.5, 644, 656
    Penitential ('*Poenitentiale Pseudo-Egberti*')*   59.5, 644, 656, 808e
    Various penitential texts and excerpts   59.5, 73, 388, 393, 395, 400, 459, 583.3, 644,
        656, 808, 814, 879
    Penitential articles issued after the Battle of Hastings   59, 376, 644
    See also Confession and absolution ; Ælfric of Eynsham ; Hormisdas ; Wulfstan I,
        Homilist, Canon Law Collection ; Ker, *Catalogue*, pp. 521-2
Persius, *Satirae*   195, 252, 493, 534, 535, *and see* 'Cornutus'
'Petrocellus', *see* Medicine
Petrus Damianus, Hymn   337
Philippus Presbyter, *Commentarii in librum Job*   576, 808.5, 840.5 (gloss)
Philosophia, *see* Liberal arts and sciences
Phocas, *Ars de nomine et verbo*   535
Phoenix**   257 ; *see also* Lactantius
Phoenix story*   64
Physiologus   114e
Physiologus**   257
Pirminius of Reichenau, *Scarapsus* (*Dicta Pirminii*)   583.3
Plato, *Timaeus, see* Lanfranc
Plautus, Eight comedies   497.2
Pliny the Elder, *Naturalis historia*   373e, 423e, 428.4e, 838e
Poems : Shorter Latin poems, mainly anonymous   12, 27, 28, 88, 93, 95, 114, 188, 196,
    252, 337, 342, 383, 391, 401, 483, 485, 492, 493, 496, 510, 523, 531, 535, 537, 651,
    661, 664, 682, 688, 765, 794, 805, 829.8, 845, 890, 919, 919.3, 938 ; *see also* Cambridge
    Songs, *and especially* Index II
Poems** : Shorter poems of the Exeter Book   257
Pompeius, *Commentum artis Donati*   933e
Pompeius Trogus, *see* Justinus
Pontificals   40, 46, 51, 143f, 157f, 214.3, 286, 302, 313, 314, 376, 397, 406.5, 468f,
    525f, 585, 875.2f, 879, 896, 922, 923, 936.7f, *and see* Pontificale Romano-
    Germanicum
Pontificale Romano-Germanicum   51, 73e, 376, 406.5
Pontifical services and prayers   29, 70, 155, 223, 363, 376, 400, 688, 742, 914

Psalter manuscripts
    Psalterium Gallicanum   77, 104, 106, 148, 250f, 270, 304°, 334, 378°, 407°, 422,
        425, 430, 499°, 517°, 617, 655, 740°, 754, 764.1f, 842.5(?), 847.5f, 912, 920,
        939
    Psalterium Hebraicum   255.5, 754, 876.5f
    Psalterium Romanum   4°, 9f, 125f, 141f°, 212.8f, 291°, 306, 381°, 422, 451°, 641,
        788f, 790, 808.6f, 862, 891
    Breviate Psalter   28
    See also Alfred ; Kentish Psalm ; Paris Psalter
Ptolemy (Claudius Ptolemaeus), *Preceptum canonis Ptolemaei*   428.4

De quattuor clavibus sapientiae   401, 903
Quodvultdeus of Carthage, *Adversus quinque haereses* (*Sermo* 10)   710

Radulf of Liège and Ragimbold of Cologne, Letters on geometry   886
Ragimbold of Cologne, *see* Radulf of Liège
Rainbow, Note on   380
Records   15^{+}*, 21*, 56*, 83*, 102*, 134*, 135*, 139*, 266*, 278, 279$^{(*)}$, 302.2, 307.6,
    327*, 362$^{(*)}$, 374*, 412*, 413, 432*, 447*, 521*, 554*, 585*, 592, 672^{+}*, 774* ;
    see also Charters, Donation inscription, Manumissions
Regula S. Benedicti, *see* Benedict of Nursia
Regularis Concordia   59e, 332, 363°, 925e ; 65f*, 332e*
Relics, Lists of   44*, 466, 500, 530*
Remigius of Auxerre, Commentaries, and glosses from his commentaries, on :
    Boethius, *De consolatione Philosophiae*   12, 23, 193, 533, 671, 776, 823, 829, 887,
        899, 901
    Disticha Catonis   120e, 664
    Donatus, *Ars minor*   775
    Martianus Capella   127f, 428.4e, 490, 700.1f
    Priscian, *Institutio de nomine, pronomine et verbo*   326
    Sedulius, *Carmen paschale* and Hymns   120, 652f, 735
    (?) Apocalypse (abbreviated)   217 (by Haimo of Auxerre?)
Remigius Favius (?), *Carmen de ponderibus et mensuris*   27, 185
Responsoriale   663f
Resting-places of English saints*   65.5, 500
Rhetoric   677.6, *and see* Beda, *De schematibus et tropis* ; Cassiodorus, *In Psalmos* ;
    Cicero, *De inventione* ; Martianus Capella
Richard of Préaux, *In Genesin*   162.6, 504.8
Riddles   12, 252, 433.3, 829.8, 898 ; 257** ; *see also* Aldhelm, Bonifatius, Eusebius,
    Symphosius, Tatwine
*Riming Poem***   257
Robert II of France, Letters   230
Roman emperors, Lists of   43, 332, 373, 486
Roman imperial dignitaries, Note on   223

Romulus, *see* 'Aesopus'
Royal genealogies and regnal lists of Anglo-Saxon kings
    All kingdoms 56, 373, 906.5
    Anglian kings 385
    East Saxon kings 282
    West Saxon kings* 52, 102, 282, 357, 364, 500
Rubisca (Hisperic poem) 12, 903
Rufinus of Aquileia
    De benedictionibus patriarcharum 230e
    Historia monachorum 761
    See also Basil the Great, Pseudo-Clement, Eusebius of Caesarea, Origenes, Sextus
        Pythagoraeus
Ruin** 257

Sacramentaries 39e, 76, 132.4f, 202f?, 255f, 263.5f, 292f, 400, 498.2f, 498.6f, 522f,
    547f, 567f, 585, 636f, 650f, 774.6f, 791f, 810f, 836.5f, 856.3f, 867, 893.5f, 921,
    929f, 933.5f
Saint-Bertin, Poem on the Abbey of 485
St. Peter's in Rome, Dimensions of 56, 90, 363*, 385, 451
Saints' lives, anonymous, in Latin : Vitae, miraculae, translationes ; also Poems on saints
    Collections 36, 215, 344, 351, 378.5, 388, 433.2, 434.5, 508, 791.3f, 869, 898 ; *see*
        also Legendaries
    Individual saints (Lives not in collections) :
            Ælfgyfu 775 ; Æthelthryth 190, 775 ; Æthelwold 927 ; Aichardus 804 ;
            Alexius 865.3 ; Bartholomaeus 136 ; Basil 260 ; Bavo 804f ; Birinus
            308.2f, 927 ; Ceolfrid 433 ; Christophorus 885.5 ; Cuthbert 781 ;
            Dionysius, Rusticus et Eleutherius 844 ; Eadgyth 775 ; Eadward King
            and Martyr 427, 775 ; Eustachius 775 ; Furseus 351 ; Judoc 474.5 ;
            Juliana 433.3, 885.5 ; Justus 819f ; Katherina 411.7 ; Kenelm 775 ;
            Laurentius 255, 379.5 ; Macarius Romanus 620.3 ; Margareta 885.5,
            930.5 ; Mauritius 99f ; Mellitus 74 ; Nicholas 373, 434.5 ; Philibert
            781, 804 ; Quintinus 885.6 ; Romanus 535 ; Seven Sleepers 361 ;
            380 (their names) ; Swithun 496 ; Tancred 434.5 ; Thais 761 ;
            Theophilus 433.3 ; Torhtred 434.5 ; Tova 434.5 ; Walaric 804
    See also : the full contents of the collections listed above, of legendaries
    and other liturgical books, and the saints' lives by known authors
Saints' lives and homilies for saints' days, anonymous, in Old English* :
    Andreas 64, 905 ; Augustine of Canterbury (Deposition) 50 ; Christophorus
    355, 399 ; Euphrosyne 339 ; Eustace 339 ; Guthlac, *see* Felix ; John the Baptist
    905 ; Kentish royal saints 500, 518f ; Machutus, *see* Bili of Alet ; Margareta 363 ;
    Martin 905, 941 ; Mary of Egypt 262f, 339, 355 ; Michael 39, 905 ; Mildred 310,
    518f, 905 ; Pantaleon 406 ; Paulinus of York 569 ; Peter and Paul 905 ; Seven
    Sleepers 339, 355 ; Veronica, *see Vindicta Salvatoris*
    See also Ælfric, *Catholic Homilies*, Homilies, Lives of Saints ; *Andreas*** ;
    Cynewulf, *Elene***, *Juliana***

Sallust, *Bellum Jugurthinum* 88.5f
Sanctus, in Greek 334, 903
Scholica Graecarum glossarum 489, 541
Seafarer* 257
Sedulius
    Carmen paschale 12, 53, 253°, 491, 652f, 824.5, 890, 903
    Hymns 12, 53, 253, 491, 824.5, 890, 903 ; *see also* Hymnals
    Letters to Macedonius 53, 253, 824.5, 890, 903
    Poems on Sedulius 12, 253, 491, 890, 903
    See also Remigius of Auxerre
Sentences, *see* Maxims
Sequences (not in graduals or tropers) 7, 56, 94, 100, 131, 431, 433.2f, 435e, 583, 844
Serenus (Quintus Serenus*), Liber medicinalis* 884
Sergius, *Explanationes in Donatum* 933
Sergius I, pope, Bull 358*
Serlo of Bayeux, *Contra monachos* 535
Service books, not identified, and Liturgica, not in service books 136.5f, 255f, 333,
    529.1, 538, 557, 848?
Servius, *In Aeneida* 849.6f, 919e
Seven Wonders of divine origin 516
Seven Wonders of the World 114, 516
Severus, *De septem gradibus ecclesiae* 516
Sextus Placitus, *Liber medicinae ex animalibus* 402*, 421e*, 549, 633*, 831.4
Sextus Pythagoreus (Rufinus), *Sententiae* 512
Sibylline prophecies 53, 114, 536, 805
Sigeric archbishop, his journey to Rome 373
Sign language, monastic, Treatise on* 363
Simplicius of Montecassino, (?) Introductory poem to *Benedicti Regula* 189
Sins, list of 189
Sisbertus Toletanus, *Lamentum paenitentiae* 699
Smaragdus of Saint-Mihiel
    Diadema monachorum 8, 31, 41 701.5
    Expositio in Regulam S. Benedicti 3, 883
    Expositio libri comitis 539, 762
Pseudo-Smaragdus
    Monitory poems 12, 478
    Opus monitorium 478
Solinus, *Collectanea* 35f, 439
Solomon and Saturn* 110
Solomon and Saturn** 39f, 110
Solomon's gold, Note on* 435
Somniale Danielis 363°, 380, 498.1f
Soranus of Ephesus, *De digestionibus* 498.7
Pseudo-Soranus, *Quaestiones medicinales* 12e
Soul and Body** 257, 941

Statius
  Achilleis 535
  Thebais 12e, 151, 497, 766f
  Vita Statii 497
Stephen of Ripon, *Vita S. Wilfridi* 390
Stones and metals, Excerpts on 230e
Suetonius, *De vita Caesarum* 281.3e
Sulpicius Severus
  Vita S. Martini 264, 296, 782f, 915
  Epistolae 264, 296 ; *Epistola III* : 782, 915
  Dialogi 264, 296, 915
Pseudo-Sulpicius Severus, *Tituli metrici de S. Martino* 296
Summons to prayer** 65
Sunday letter* 363
Syagrius, *Regulae definitionum contra haereticos prolatae* 164e
Sylloge of Latin inscriptions (Bishop Mildred's collection) 938
Symbolum 'Clemens Trinitas' 296
Symphosius, *Aenigmata* 12, 252, 478, 493

Tabernacle (Jewish tabernacle, see Exodus xxv-xxxi, xxxv-xl), Dimensions of 56, 90, 385, 451
Tatian (Latin version by Victor of Capua), *Diatessaron* 827.6
Tatwine, *Aenigmata* 12, 478
De taxone liber 402*, 421*, 549, 633*, 831.4
Te Deum 381° ; *see* Canticles
Temple (of Solomon at Jerusalem), Dimensions of 56, 90, 363°, 385, 451, 882
Terence
  Comedies 669.6
  Vita Terentii 669.6
Tertullian, *Apologeticum* 653.2
Themistius, *De decem categoriis* (Latin version) 67, 200.5f, 795
Theodore of Canterbury, Poem 90
Theodore of Mopsuestia, *Commentarii in Epistolas Pauli* 900.5f
Theodulf of Orléans
  Capitula 66, 66*, 73e, 608.1e⁺*
  De ordine baptismi 475
  De processione Spiritus Sancti 710
Theodulus, *Ecloga* 535
Pseudo-Theophilus, Sergius and Hyginus, *see* Saints' lives in Latin : Macarius Romanus
Thieves hanged with Christ, Names of 363*
Thirty silver coins of Judas, *see De triginta argenteos*
Tonary 185.1
Tours, Note on the basilica at 296
Tribal hidage 435*
De triginta argenteos (of Judas), Note on* 435

Trinity, Treatise on 889
Tropers 116, 309, 433.1f, 597

Unidentified texts 136, 214.6f, 241.3f, 255f, 474e, 670.5f, 808.4f, 893.8f, 943.2f*
Usuard, *see* Martyrologium

Valerius Maximus, *Facta et dicta memorabilia* 281.3e
Vegetius, *Epitome rei militaris* 325.1, 439
Venantius Fortunatus, *Carmina* 2e, 120e, 142f, 284
Verba seniorum (from *Vitas Patrum*, bk. V) 281e, 359e*, 389e, 761e, 808.2e
Vercelli Homilies* 941
Vergil
    Aeneid 12e, 477f, 503f, 648f, 919 ; *see also* Pseudo-Ovid, Servius
    Bucolica 919
    Georgica 258e, 648f, 919 ; *see also* Pseudo-Ovid
Pseudo-Vergil
    Aetna 27
    Culex 27, 919
    Poem (SK 10279) 114, 919
    Poem (SK 16845) 12, 253, 919
Versification (Latin metrics)
    Glossary of metrical terms 438
    Table of metrical feet 765
    See also Aldhelm, *Epistola ad Acircium* ; Beda, *De arte metrica* ; Israel the
        Grammarian ; Lupus of Ferrières
Victor of Capua, *see* Tatian
Victor of Vita, *Historia persecutionis Africanae provinciae* 200, 251.5
Victorinus of Pettau
    De fabrica mundi 516
    In Apocalypsin (rec. by Jerome) 1
Vigilius Thapsensis
    Contra Arianos, Sabellianos, Photinianos 137, 552
    (?) *Contra Felicianum* 266.5, 268.2, 749, 750.5
Pseudo-Vigilius Thapsensis, *Solutiones obiectionum Arianorum* 552
Vindicta Salvatoris 15*, 62*, 930.5
De vindictis magnorum peccatorum 459
The Virgin Mary
    Life of the Virgin 175.5
    Homilies* 39, 64, 638, 905, 941
    Age of the Virgin, Note on 363*, 380*, 411*, 500*
    Immaculate conception, Note on 180
    See also Masses ; Office of the Virgin
Virtues and Vices, Tracts on 470°, 523.5 ; *see also* Sins
Visio Baronti 351

Index II
Shorter Latin poems (including liturgical verse compositions), mainly anonymous

The following Indexes do not include the contents of collections (Cambridge Songs, Hymnals, Tropers).

Index IIA
Poems recorded in Schaller and Könsgen, *Initia carminum Latinorum saeculo undecimo antiquiorum* (SK)

SK	Handlist	SK	Handlist
33	450, 903	2143	220, 342
151	428.4	2326	12
177	12	2361	88
188	337	2425	95, 196
251	12	2501	483
302	794	2593	12, 903
412	28	2652	188
474	927	2659	38, 680
588	450	2799	938
591	927	3197	27
605	246	3448	188
638	196, 829, 919	3476	938
685	333	3536	933
708	450	3544	381
853	612	3618	12, 765
989	661	3639	485
1005	805	3727	258
1012	688	4088	538
1013	333	4297	88
1037	845	4382	120
1112	120	4455	938
1319	474.5	4458	794
1409a	12	4819	805
1417	70	4939	38, 680
1443	496, 927	5349	120
1479	765	5374	938
1530	927	5533	27
1663	482	5725	321
1701	196	5836	12
1716	258, 612	5868	938
1904	491	5925	536
2086a	12	6193	193

SK	Handlist	SK	Handlist
6489	258	10768	392
6618	938	10856	12, 120
6687	12	10904	12
6873	938	10905	903
7122	938	10920	7
7173	56	10972	175, 188
7221	919	10988	12, 478
7355	919.3	11017	59
7445	28	11045	927
7449	865.2	11084	765, 903
7486	53	11297	93, 510
7632	258	11339	12
7704	938	11355	829
7810	12, 478	11580	474.5
7891	443	11608	12, 903
7896	428.4	11969	12, 765
8093	664, 903	12104	27, 185
8331	845	12366	301
8353	903	12423	886
8406	938	12491	258
8495	114, 536, 805	12515	392
8630	100	12524	258
8785	514	12542	919
8793	514	12551	12, 829.8, 903
8931	258, 612	12559	258
8933	612	12594	12, 478, 661
9224	56	12730	381, 523
9405	938	12765	12
9446	531	12954	253
9447	243	13113	845
9481	784.5	13123	829
9504	450	13209	938
9505	12	13280	383
9568	450	13285	189
9575	136	13567	325
9879	844	13757	120
9929	252	13822	765
9993	938	14026	612
10021	433.2	14230	196
10046	93, 688	14234	381
10204	12	14294	362
10279	114, 919	14392	765, 903
10728	381	14414	252

SK	Handlist		SK	Handlist
14633	12		15784	12, 253
14640	12		15860	87
14655	435		16044	12
14841	12, 253, 491, 890, 903		16100	90
14842	12, 253, 491, 890, 903		16284	12
14935	682		16396	120
15226	27		16461	188
15273	48		16714	474.5
15347	401, 903		16845	12, 253, 919
15514	938		17048	306.5
15583	890		17050	844
15611	938		17136	12
15627	381		17321	938
15745	28, 421			

Index IIB
Poems recorded in Walther, *Initia Carminum ac Versuum Medii Aevi Posterioris Latinorum*, but not in Schaller-Könsgen, *Initia*

Walther	Handlist		Walther	Handlist
2123	535		14029	535
4803	919.3		14116	664
11179	230		14284	252
11654	252		14648	481
12589	230		14969	230
12877a	264		18791	775
13383	252		20298	844

Index IIC
Poems edited in *Analecta Hymnica*, but not recorded in Schaller-Könsgen or Walther, *Initia Carminum ac Versuum*

AH 11.67	Handlist 865.1
AH 11.68	Handlist 865.1
AH 48.52	Handlist 337

Index IID
Manuscripts with poems not recorded in Schaller-Könsgen and Walther, *Initia Carminum ac Versuum*, and not edited in *Analecta Hymnica*

Handlist nos. 7, 23, 74, 94, 114, 188, 196, 230, 252, 282, 333, 342, 342.3, 354, 379.5, 382, 389, 391, 401, 427, 483, 492, 496, 612, 651, 775, 829, 829.8, 844, 865.1, 890, 903, 927